D1484260

CODFISH, DOGFISH, MERMAIDS AND FRANK

Coming of Age on the Open Ocean

By
Skip DeBrusk

The Reginald vanFenwick Press
Stoughton, MA

CARVER PUBLIC LIBRARY

In certain instances the names and identities of specific individuals and establishments have been changed to protect their privacy.

Front Cover from left to right: Skip, Frank, Rolly and Eddie.

Back Cover photograph of Skip courtesy of Victor Oliver

Many of the Photographs originally appeared in the Old Colony Memorial Newspaper. Reprinted with Permission.

Copyright © 2007 by Skip DeBrusk

All rights reserved. No part of this book may be reproduced or transmitted in any form or by any means, mechanical or electronic, without the written permission of The Reginald vanFenwick Press. For information on special educational discounts and bulk purchases, please contact The Reginald vanFenwick Press, 6 Chase Circle, Stoughton, MA 02072, or email at info@vanfenwickpress.com

Contact the author at sdebrusk@comcast.net

Library of Congress Control Number: 2006926735
ISBN: 0-9728169-4-1

Second Edition

Published by
The Reginald vanFenwick Press
Stoughton, MA

Manufactured in the United States of America

Dedications

If the oceans are vast and difficult to measure, so, too, is my love and devotion to Carolyn.

This book is also dedicated to commercial fishermen everywhere.

Chapter Headings

Introduction

Plymouth, Massachusetts, 1951

The gentle northeast wind with its exotic perfume of seaweed, mud flats and beach roses drifted over the State Pier and helped take my mind off the shouting match I'd just had with my father. I was fifteen years old, headed for a job interview.

For the past five summers I'd worked on the *Louise*, a party boat that left Plymouth Harbor each morning. Despite the ten-hour days, it was considered a child's job. Charlie Rose, owner and captain of the *Louise*, enjoyed smoking a cigarette down to a half-inch butt, peeling off the thin paper and chewing the remaining tobacco until it was time for the next one. By noon he'd start nipping from his bottle of "cough medicine," which I eventually discovered was Four Roses Whiskey. When we handled parties of twenty-five heavy drinkers arriving with twenty cases of beer and a case of whiskey (already partially consumed during the early morning bus ride from Worcester or Pawtucket) Charlie would need more medicine. Around 4:00 he'd say, "Skippy, get those damn fish cleaned fast as you can, then get up here and take the wheel!"

Today I would be meeting with Captain Frank Savery, owner of the *J. L. Stanley And Sons*. Not just a top moneymaker, the *Stanley's* reputation for order, cleanliness and safety attracted the best crewmembers. Frank Savery lived four houses up the street from us. I knew very little about him except that he had spent seven years in the U.S. Military Prison at Alcatraz, married a beautiful woman, and became one of the two best skippers in the small tourist and fishing community of Plymouth, Massachusetts.

I rounded the familiar corner that led onto the State Pier, less than 50 yards from my home. I'd made the turn so many times that I no longer saw details. I failed to see Myles Standish surveying the progress of latter-day Pilgrims from his monument high on a hill, across the bay in Duxbury.

The *Stanley* had tied up on the south side of the dock, the only boat there. But as I approached the edge of the wharf, I heard shouting: *slime loving, scum sucking, spineless jellyfish–insipid, ice age, imbecilic idiot!*

I froze. Was this the way Frank treated his crew? I stood for a moment, unsure of my next move. I wanted to arrive early, or at least on time, but didn't want to interrupt anything. It seemed best to wait until things cooled off, so I stalled by walking around the dock. Until that moment, it hadn't occurred to me to be nervous.

I tried to settle my nerves by planning what I would tell Frank about my experiences on the *Louise*. Charlie Rose had taught me well. "There's always something to do on a boat," he said. "When you see something that needs to be done, do it, do it now and do it well! Don't wait to be asked, do it with a smile. And never, ever complain." Not always an easy task when you have two dozen drunken fishermen on board! He also impressed upon me the importance of knowing where everything was located. "Skippy," he would preach, "lives depend on knowing, knowing without thinking, where a certain piece of equipment is stored." As on all good boats, the credo was safety first. For all the whiskey consumed, the *Louise* was a safe boat.

When I returned, I stood and listened. It seemed that some of the intensity had drained from the cursing voice. I paused, and to my surprise, heard poetry: *Were I with thee, Wild nights would be our luxury!*

Now I really didn't know what to do. So I turned and made another circuit around the dock. Just what was I in for, anyway? By now I was late and couldn't put it off any longer. Apprehensively, I headed toward the deck.

Poetry At Sea

Oh, the gallant fisher's life! It is the best of any;
'Tis full of pleasure, void of strife, and 'tis beloved by many.

–Izaak Walton, *The Angler*

I'd stalled just long enough. As I looked over the edge of the pier, I saw Frank alone on deck, looking around, stretching. I hurried down the ladder and introduced myself. He reached out and with a smile, shook my hand the way he would with a grownup.

"Hi Skip, let's go below and talk."

"Okay." I liked that he hadn't used the diminutive "Skippy." As I followed him into the fo'castle I said, "Sorry I'm late. I heard voices and didn't want to butt in."

"Voices? Oh." He chuckled. "Yeah." Lighting a cigarette, he appraised me, a skinny, eager kid; not much taller than 5 foot five and hovering at about 110 pounds on a good day. "You like Emily Dickinson?"

"Uh, well, sometimes. If I can sort of understand her."

"Look her up in the library, you'll enjoy *Wild Nights*. I believe there is poetry to everything: architecture, mechanics, comedy, tragedy, mathematics, nature, everything–and that includes cursing. Spilling your verbal guts out all over the bloody deck."

I was puzzled. "You mean you weren't talking to anyone? You were just swearing and reciting poetry... by yourself?"

His laugh was easy, confident. "I like to keep in practice. Anyway, I'm looking for someone for the summer. The pay will be a half share and the person will be expected to do all the duties on deck plus help the cook–wash the dishes, keep the fo'castle clean. Stuff you learned on the *Louise*, I imagine."

"Yes, sir." I was flattered that he knew my experience. Plymouth in the fifties was a small town, the kind of place where everyone knew everyone else's business; even things you didn't want them to know.

"Do you consider yourself lucky?" he asked.

"Sure."

"Why?"

"Because I'm lucky to have this opportunity to talk with you about a job that I really want."

He smiled. "Okay, any other reasons?"

I didn't even have to think. "The tuna I harpooned last year was definitely more luck than skill, but everyone on the *Frances Elizabeth* made a little extra money that day."

"I heard about that," he said. "Word got around that some scrawny assed kid managed to stick an 800-pound tuna and set the dart deep enough to actually land it."

"Louie Rivers invited me along on a busman's holiday and I was the one free to play with the tuna while the rest of the crew was working."

"Remind me, what did I hear about you and a half-dead whale washing ashore in the middle of tourist season?" he asked, and from the twinkle in his eye, I could tell he remembered the whole story.

"Well, a couple of friends and I herded this injured pilot whale around the boat mooring area. It ended up right in front of Plymouth Rock. There were hundreds of sightseers, all more interested in the big 'fish' than the little rock. We tried to save it, kept it covered in wet burlap. Twenty minutes after it came ashore, the police showed up at my mother's house to tell her the town was going to charge her $600 dollars to remove it. My mother chewed them out, then went to the beach to chew me out."

He laughed. "What happened?"

"Nothing. She took one look at my face and didn't say a word. I was, well, I was pretty upset. As soon as I got close to the whale I could see it had been shot at least four times. The wounds were at first hard to see due to the thickness of the skin. Someone good with a gun had cracked off several quick shots that ran diagonally along its back before the animal dove to safety. Maybe someone mistook it for a shark or something. But probably they just wanted a little live target practice."

Frank sighed. I saw the circumstances bothered him too, and suddenly the story wasn't funny anymore. "Did you by any chance see any markings on it?" he asked.

"As a matter of fact, yeah. I still remember it said TYD-32. Carved right into its skin."

"Probably belonged to the Navy or the CIA. They branded whales, strapped explosives on their backs and sent them out on underwater demolition work or suicide missions. Living torpedoes."

"Well all I know is, it took a long time to talk Charlie into towing it off the beach!" No need to tell Frank how much Charlie hated doing anything that didn't turn into money. Not that there was anything wrong with that–he was no different from any other fisherman struggling to make a living. But the two hours it took to convince him was a picnic compared to asking my dad for $600. As a matter of fact, my mom and I made sure my dad never heard about it until after it was over and the whale had been dragged off the beach and returned to the sea.

"So," Frank said, "you quick with your hands?"

"Definitely."

"Good. We're steaking whiting and I need someone with good hands. We chop alota heads in a day."

"I'm fast," I bragged.

"Then whaddya say Skip, would you like to do some serious fishing with us? I think you'd make a great addition to our crew."

"Yes! Thank you."

We shook hands again. For the first time I noticed he was missing fingers.

"You can start the day after school lets out," he said.

"I can start tomorrow," I said. "I don't care that much for school."

But he shook his head. "Education is important. You'll come to find that out."

"But what they teach us is so stupid! Stuff I'll never need to know! Believe me, Frank, I can learn more in the real world."

"You think that now, but trust me, staying in school until you graduate is the best thing you can do for yourself. Okay?"

I sighed. "Okay."

He grinned. "Nice try, though!"

Even though I set two alarms–one for 3:00 and one for 3:05–I shut them both off at 2:45 and climbed out of bed, too excited to sleep. I dressed quietly so I wouldn't wake my mother. Waking my father was not a consideration as I slipped past him lying on the couch, dead to the world. At 3:15 I stepped aboard the *Stanley* for my first day as a commercial fisherman, and the clean, salty smell of early morning made it one of the most exhilarating moments of my life.

Rolly Bedard, the man in charge of the engines, was already there.

He had the gasoline kicker on and switched it over to start the main source of power, a 115 horsepower Caterpillar diesel with a four to one reduction gear. The reduction gears slowed the *Stanley* down, but provided more power to haul the net over the bottom. I loved the sound; it spoke of pure, masculine energy. This was not the little engine that could; this was Big Daddy, whose large, eight-cylinder voice was the epitome of competence and confidence.

Eddie Fairweather arrived next, heard the main engine running and threw off the spring lines. Everyone was on board well before 3:30.

Frank introduced me as the new man for the summer. As I shook hands with the other members of the crew, I promised myself the *Stanley* would get every ounce of manhood I possessed.

As we left the pier and headed down the channel, Eddie carried coffee up to Frank at the wheel and then said, "Come on Skip, let's go below and grab another hour of sleep."

The fo'castle was typical of an eastern-rigged dragger; a doghouse covered the entrance and protected the nearly vertical ladder descending into the forward quarter of the boat. Coming in from the dark it seemed bright, warm and inviting, with no hint of the cool early morning air. Troy Griffin, our cook, had built a small wood fire in the black Shipmate stove, and the aroma of fresh coffee mixed with hints of fish, bilge water, diesel fuel, bedding, garlic and several other unidentifiable odors that were not unpleasant. The fo'castle was immaculate, as clean as my mother's kitchen. Three bunks on each side followed the contour of the boat and allowed just enough clearance for a person to crawl in.

Eddie pointed to the top bunk on the starboard side. "That's yours, Skip." He pulled off his moccasins, climbed into the bottom berth and immediately fell sleep.

I lay down on the old blue striped mattress that was on top of several half-inch pine boards. The planks had no support on the bottom except where they met at the head and foot. They moved just the right amount, with a soft creak, in unison with the boat and the person in the bunk. I listened to the water swishing by just inches from my head, and the powerful, commanding vibration of the Caterpillar engine pushing us forward into the advancing dawn. Who could sleep!

And yet I jumped half an hour later when a large, callused hand on my ankle shook me awake.

"Rise and shine, Beautiful," Eddie said.

I squeezed out of the bunk, pulled on my boots and hurried up the ladder to the organized bustle of pre-dawn activity. Everybody and everything was in motion, with Frank at the wheel.

"Let's get the net going," Frank said, and then asked Eddie, "Is the bag tied?"

Eddie leaned over to touch the slipknot. "Yup."

Frank turned to me and explained that checking with Eddie was part of a time-honored routine. "I've seen fishermen throw the net out with the pucker strings untied, and at the end of the tow they haul it in, empty. Fish go in the front and out the back, never even know they were in the net!"

Eddie added, "Happened on the *Liberty II* once, and the rumor went 'round that John Pinto tried to throw the person responsible overboard!"

I laughed, and then got serious. Eddie, functioning as the unofficial first mate, senior deck hand and twine man in charge of the 35-foot whiting net, showed me where to stand to throw the body and wings of the net overboard, then sent me back to the stern gallows.

"Watch out for the 5/8 inch towing wire!"

I already knew the danger. When the doors aren't on the bottom, they hang from the appropriately named gallows. All the strain of dragging the net is focused on the gallows, which are securely braced onto the main structure of the boat's hull. I waited for the quick hook up link and attached the doors to the towing wire.

Doors on a dragger are at the entrance to the net and everything that goes into the net passes through the doors. They are used in pairs, and are formally called otter boards. They weigh 500 pounds each and have a pair of iron brackets that cause them to veer away from each other.

"We're in a large half bowl of mud roughly five miles in diameter. We'll make this first tow a short one to see how we're doing," Frank said.

With the net down, we hurried through breakfast–eggs, fried linguica and toast. Troy didn't have a percolator so he boiled the coffee. Intrigued, I watched him throw in some eggshells.

Frank laughed at the look on my face. "A little hen shit makes it nice and smooth, removes the bitter taste."

"I don't mind the taste," Eddie told me, "It's the damn feathers!"

The net had been on the bottom for forty minutes and even my inexperienced senses felt the difference in our forward motion. Eddie replaced Frank in the wheelhouse. With great care Frank showed me how to use the four-foot iron rod to steer the cable evenly on to the winch.

"Lots of fishermen have slipped forward and instinctively put their hands out to break their fall. This revolving drum and the incoming wire cuts off whatever comes in between–a finger, a hand, a wrist–or any other extremity."

"Didja hear what happened to La Verde?" Rolly asked me. I shook my head. "He runs a trap boat, the *Four Aces*. Just before he unloaded his catch, using the winch on Town Pier, he rolled down his hip boots below the knee. Suddenly a strap of the boot snarled in the winch and tore off his leg just below the femur. Art Caranci took his leather belt, applied a tourniquet and saved LaVerde's life. LaVerde is sitting in Jordan Hospital right now with a fractured shoulder, some nasty face bruises, and half his left leg missing. It happened less than ten minutes from the hospital. If it'd happened out here, two hours away not counting time to haul back the net or any complications, story would've ended differently. He's one lucky son of a bitch."

"Whenever you pick up this iron bar, think of LaVerde," Frank said. "He was on a solid dock, it wasn't rough, it wasn't slippery, and he hadn't been up all night. Out here that little slip would have cost him his life. But all he lost was half a leg; learn from LaVerde."

I nodded soberly. It was always good to be reminded that danger could spring up anytime.

The doors came up clanking and crashing and were uncoupled to allow the rest of the net to come on board. As the body of the net approached the side of the boat, dazed whiting swam out of the mouth. I could tell there was a large number of fish because the floats were having trouble staying on the surface.

"Great haul," Frank said, "but it won't always be this way." I watched as he grew pensive. "Right now, fish are everywhere. Commercial fishing slowed when World War II began, with so many young guys in the service, while older men were encouraged to work in war-related manufacturing. Some were discouraged by fuel being rationed. Other fishermen I know wouldn't go out because they were afraid of enemy submarines, so the fish stocks really increased. But we've got plenty of fuel and the Koreans don't have any subs over here, not yet any way, so let's enjoy what we have."

Our first tow came back as a split and a heist, which means there were too many fish to bring aboard with one lift of the bag. Under these circumstances, the net is split into segments and the bag at the end of the net is emptied as many times as necessary. With two bags of fish on the deck, and the net reset, we began scooping up fish into a long, waist high wooden box with five cutting boards running across the top.

The process was simple: pick up a whiting from the box, lay it on the cutting board facing out, and cut off its head. Add a slight outward twist and the fish's head along with its internal organs all go overboard. One vertical cut, ending with the outward motion, and a perfectly processed fish is ready for market.

"Gets to be downright monotonous, really boring after a while," Eddie warned me. "Cut as many heads as fast as you can, but keep your fingers away from the knife! When we pass some of the Portuguese boats you'll see how fast they are. But right now, don't go for speed. Just keep the box full of fish and your fingers safe."

Keeping the cutting box full sounded like a straightforward assignment, but the box seemed higher and the fish grew heavier as the day progressed. At least switching between cutting heads and filling the box allowed for a change. I tried to keep the other crew members busy cutting until I came up to speed. For the first hour, the fifteen-inch knife did not feel especially heavy but I knew by the end of the day it would feel like a Sherman Tank. Our next tow produced even more than the first. Silver scales glistened everywhere in the bright sun, in the ocean; spilling out of the net, on our deck, under my shirt.

For the rest of the morning we set the net, towed for thirty to forty minutes, hauled back and cut heads while the net went back over for more. We made sure that our cut fish were washed quickly and put in the hold to be covered with ice.

We squeezed in a lunch of Italian cold cuts, hastily washed down with Coca Cola, in between hauling up the net, emptying, and re-setting it. Around 2:00 we passed the *Jimmy Boy*, and Eddie said, "Watch this." As we passed port side to port side, I saw the men on the *Jimmy Boy* were cutting many more than we were.

Frank stuck his head out the pilothouse window. "Look at those heads fly! That's the finest kind, the very finest kind of head chopping! Each man has a head in the air all the time."

Frank's comment made me want to work harder and faster. At 3:30 we made one last tow, filled the deck to the gunwales, and Frank started to steam slowly towards Plymouth. He put two little rope loops over opposing spokes of the wheel and joined us at the cutting box. We paused to wash the net outside the Gurnet by towing it behind us on the surface without using the doors. Then it was full speed ahead to Plymouth. We were unloaded and re-iced by 8:00 that evening, and I made my way home to set the two alarms again for 3:00 and 3:05 a.m., this time afraid my exhaustion might allow me to sleep through a single warning.

Thumbs Up

Fish long, fish hard, come home with the boat full
But never forget who is really in charge out there.

Fisherman's Credo

Excruciating pain in my right wrist made me groan as I reached to shut off the alarm clock. What the hell? It wouldn't move at all! Gritting my teeth, as I got dressed, I couldn't imagine ever being able to use it again.

At 3:15 I arrived at the dock and awkwardly made my way down the ladder one handed.

Rolly stepped out of the shadows when he heard my approach, and witnessed my descent with sympathy. "Coffee's on," he said.

"Thanks."

I followed him into the fo'castle. Eddie and Troy were already there. As casually as I could, I helped myself to a cup of coffee with my left hand, took a sip, then set the cup down and reached for a donut. My right hand with it's throbbing wrist hid in full retreat, pressed against my side.

"You okay?" Eddie asked.

"Sure." I ate a whole donut so that my left hand would be free again and reached for my coffee.

"Wrist sore?"

"Little bit."

"Listen." He put his hand on my shoulder. "I'm really sorry, but I forgot to tell you yesterday, one thing you must never ever do is cut whiting all day and then pound your pudding at night. Either one is okay, but the human body can't withstand the strain of both."

Solemnly, Rolly offered me a piece of mending twine. "It's hard for me to remember not to hack my carrot, so I tie a piece of string on my manly pride. Helps remind me, whiting or beating my meat, but *never both.*"

"Very funny."

They laughed as Frank joined us. He took one look at me and said,

"How's the wrist, Old Dog?"

I'd never been called "old" anything, but before I could answer he went on, "I can't believe that these excellent examples of exotic excrement, these sniveling sedentary slime suckers didn't warn you about the dangers of steaking whiting! Well now you know, it's one or the other. Serve humanity and deliver silver hake to the poor, huddled masses of New York City, or stay home and choke your chicken."

"I told him about the twine trick," Rolly said, and Eddie nodded, grinning.

"Thanks, guys," I said, reaching for another donut. "I appreciate your words of wisdom."

Frank smiled. "You got a bad case of the grip. Take it easy until you feel better. Okay, let's go."

Leaving the dock we cruised down the silver, black channel, out to where the fish were knee deep. I crawled into my bunk, wincing as I automatically reached out to pull myself up with my right hand. Somehow I'd pick up that steaking knife and chop heads. If nothing else, I'd keep the box full of whiting for the others.

Rocking gently in my cradle of acceptance, I realized that my initiation into the fishing fraternity was underway. In this macho, show no fear world, the men supported me, considered me part of the crew. Screw the pain, never complain. Sometimes you need to chew on it before you spit it out.

Our first set that morning produced another mountain of whiting. With fish on the deck, we started to work while Frank went into the fo'castle looking for more coffee.

Eddie turned to me. "Your folks got a TV set?"

"Not yet."

"Too bad. You missed a great fight last night. Rocky Marciano. Standing room only in the Bird."

"Pretty good for someone who used to work in a Brockton shoe factory," Rolly said. "Might even wind up being heavyweight champion, he's got a nice winning streak going. You know, Frank used to fight."

"I heard that but I was never sure if it was true or not. What weight did he fight in?" I asked.

"I don't know, either feather or bantam weight, but he was way up there in the rankings."

"Tough guy," Eddie shook his head. "I wouldn't wanna be on the wrong end of his fist."

"Yeah," said Rolly, "but that fist and his temper are what got him in all the trouble."

"Seven years in Alcatraz," Eddie added as if I didn't know; as if every single person in town didn't know.

I stepped closer. "I always wondered what happened."

"Frank got messed up in a barroom brawl, maybe over a crap game, and knocks this big guy on the jaw. On his way down the man hits his head and dies. Because Frank's a trained boxer, he gets charged with assault with a deadly weapon."

"Frank... killed a guy?"

"Frank hit a guy and the guy died," Eddie clarified. "He didn't do it on purpose."

"Lotta stories about Frank, we're not sure if they're true or not. I heard he held up a Chinese bakery with a pistol he *borrowed* from an Army officer," Rolly put in.

"I heard he ripped off a prison guard's face with a pick axe."

"Damn!"

Rolly and Troy sharpened our knives, threw the trash fish overboard while Eddie and I filled the fish box, and together we started chopping heads. Blaring out of the wheelhouse radio came the announcement of last night's fight: *Keep your eye on this kid, the Brockton Blockbuster! He hasn't lost a single fight!* I wondered if they'd talked about Frank on the radio this way. If Eddie and Rolly, Frank's crewmates and friends didn't know the facts, who did?

"In prison, one of the few intramural sports was to curse everyone and everything," Eddie went on, an affectionate note creeping into his voice. "He loves swearing and really misses someone to practice with–sort of like a boxer missing his favorite sparing partner. Not much to do on the Rock, so he read all the books in the prison library."

"Brought to him by the warden's daughter," Rolly finished the story.

"Next best thing to being the farmer's daughter," Eddie said and they laughed.

"I heard somewhere that Frank's IQ was so high they couldn't even measure it."

"That part's true," Eddie nodded. "Genius level. He's a math wiz."

"Photographic memory," Rolly said. "And he's interested in everything. Swear to God, there's not one single thing Frank doesn't know about. He's the only person I know who can enjoy thinking so much. I like thinking about certain things, but Frank..."

"Loves to think. I wonder if that's what gives him those headaches?" Eddie asked. His gaze traveled to the fo'castle; Frank was still inside, but Eddie lowered his voice. "He's also kind of accident prone. Watches over his guys, but doesn't know we watch over him just as hard."

"Harder," Rolly said.

I nodded as Frank came back on deck. Frank only stood about five foot four, probably weighed in at 125, but somehow he appeared larger. Part of this came from his erect posture and his stride; he always seemed in a relaxed hurry. "Thanks for letting me know," I said.

The next morning I arrived before Eddie. First time! But before I had a chance to gloat, Frank said, "Eddie won't be here for a few days. He and his wife are separating and he needs to meet with bankers, lawyers and some other shore bound folks."

"So we'll be one man short?"

"No, I got a kid lined up; he begs me for a job every time I bump into him." Frank looked at his watch and frowned. "Shit, he's already late. Let's go get him."

A moonless night, cool for the time of year, made the Milky Way appear closer than normal, giving the impression that we could just as easily sail to the distant stars as to Stellwagen Bank. Usually I enjoyed the quiet beauty of nights like this, but somehow tonight felt different. I climbed into Frank's rusted 1939 Buick.

"I oughta trade this old bucket in," Frank said, "now that Detroit's building pleasure cars again. Haven't been any new ones since the beginning of the war."

"I know, my uncle would love to buy an 'all new' Buick, but that won't happen for years."

"Almost nobody in Plymouth owns one." Frank turned onto Church Street. "The best place to see a new car is on the waterfront, along the tourist haunts. Someone in the Midwest buys a new car and takes the family to do the historical tour of the Northeast."

The screech of tires and sudden accelerations with Frank's window-rattling muffler shattered the silence of the sleeping town. He parked outside the kid's apartment near the Unitarian Church, left the motor running and ran into the two-decker.

A few seconds later he reappeared. "The kid's saying a passionate farewell to his girlfriend. I told him he's got him two minutes to get his sweaty, sorry ass down here."

Sweaty is right, I thought, as the kid came running down and jumped into the back seat of the car. If he smelled this bad now, what was he going to be like after a few hours in hot oilskins?

Just before Frank was about to pull out, we heard someone playing the church organ, a jazz version of "Amazing Grace," then a skillful transition into the "St. Louis Blues" even louder than the rumbling muffler.

Frank sat motionless, captivated. "It would almost be worth going to church this morning to hear what the preacher says about this," he said after a minute, and sang along in a voice that surprised me with its full-bodied resonance. "*Red-hair woman makes a preacher leave his home.* You can bet your sweet ass somebody'll be leaving when the congregation gets a load of this."

Abandoning all hope for an early start, we lingered while the sound of the great organ swelled in volume. The music reverberated off the old stonewalls and grew louder and more boisterous, as if the organist could sense that we were outside enjoying his performance.

"Listen to that left hand!" Frank said. "The whole thing about jazz is a powerful left hand." The rest of his artistic commentary was lost in a combination of screeching tires, police sirens and the echoing organ. Not eager for another delay, Frank jammed his foot on the accelerator and the big V8 jerked us back into our seats as the flashing blue lights raced towards the church.

We arrived back at the dock and were under way as the last foot hit the deck. Frank eased us away from the dock and down the channel. Everyone except Frank and the kid rushed into the fo'castle eager for that precious extra hour of sleep.

Before we climbed into our bunks, it surprised us to see Frank come down the ladder for coffee.

"Where's the kid?" Rolly asked.

"At the wheel. He says he knows the channel. I told him I'd be right back. Usually Eddie brings me my coffee." Frank smirked, a teasing look that said, *Why didn't any of you bastards bring it to me?*

But as he started up the ladder, a sudden, sickening crash stopped the forward progress of the boat and he was thrown violently against the table. The rest of us grabbed on to anything stable while coffee mugs, dishes and gear hit the floor.

Frank regained his balance, and staggered back up the ladder. We hurried after him amidst moans, groans and unrecordable profanity. *Oh my God*, I thought; *We hit another boat! Somebody with no running lights. Where's the life ring, the life jackets...* Charlie Rose's words echoing in my mind.

However, as we reached the deck, it was a different predicament. We were completely out of the channel and hard aground.

I stood panting, waiting for my alarm to fade, trying to process what happened. There are two sets of range lights used to guide boats in and out of Plymouth at night. Leaving the harbor, the first combination is used up to the mid-point buoy. The second pair is for the last part of the east-west channel leading up to the large stationary buoy that signals a ninety-degree left turn to run parallel along Plymouth Beach. For some reason, the kid either didn't know or totally ignored these guiding lights. In the crystalline night air, we could see the two pairs of red range lights and I had never seen them so far out of line, but then, I had never been aground before. I knew this channel far better than most of the streets in Plymouth and on a beautiful night like this it seemed incomprehensible that any one could go this far astray. Fortunately, we had run bow first into a mud bank and the hardest thing under our bottom consisted of a few mussel shells, which meant no damage to the boat.

But the good news stopped there. We hit the mud flat at full throttle and the four to one reduction gear, coupled with the boat's momentum, had plowed us deeply into the mud. No amount of reverse engines helped. We launched the orange dory that served as our lifeboat, loaded our anchor, rowed out thirty yards, dropped the anchor and tried to pull ourselves free using a combination of winch, pulleys and reverse engines.

Nothing helped. The *Stanley* drew seven and a half feet of water and most of that draft lay encased in soft, sticky mud. The ebbing tide was only half out, so we faced a long wait–three hours for the tide to reach dead low and six more for high tide, when we might hope to float free. Nine hours with nothing to do.

Frank's silence became insufferable. He didn't swear or speak at all but I knew the maggots were munching on his brain. Our predicament wasn't helped by the fact that the rest of the fleet left just behind us. Gloomily I watched the other boats head out to sea, their taunts loud and clear across the water: *How's the clamming, Capt.? Channel's a little narrow here, thanks for letting us by! Ha ha ha!*

The kid looked pitiful and smelled awful. He mumbled apologies but everyone turned away. Like a terminally ill dog, it would have been an act of great kindness to shoot him right there. *Bang!* Everyone, including the kid would have felt much better.

We shoveled out the ice and pumped the bilges dry. I rowed the rest of the crew into the State Pier while Frank stayed on the *Stanley* and brought her in at high tide. We worked one man short for the next three days. We never saw the kid again.

"Here's another one for you." Rolly threw me a copy of Mickey Spillane's *Kiss me Deadly.* Page 13 had been folded down and my eyes went immediately to the scene the previous reader found so interesting. My collection of *Classic Comics* suddenly seemed as gripping as *The Dead Sea Scrolls.* Certainly *Kiss me Deadly* was nothing I'd ever checked out on any of my numerous trips to the Plymouth Town Library. It was sanctuary; an oasis that provided escape from my alcoholic father, only 300 yards from my house with noble elm trees that gave it a sense of quiet, dependable dignity. An avid reader, I usually extended the escapism by retreating to my room most evenings with a stack of books.

One of my goals was to read everything in the public library with a nautical theme. Some were tough going, like *Fishes of the Gulf Of Maine*, *Celestial Navigation* or *The Odyssey*. Others I read two or three times: *Swordfisherman Jim*, *Twenty Thousand Leagues Under The Sea*, *Kon-Tiki*, *Mutiny on the Bounty* and *The Deep Sea's Toll.*

The librarians knew me well and liked to recommend books. However, to the best of my knowledge, there wasn't anything in the Plymouth Library that came close to the literature favored by the crew of the *Stanley*. I had tried some of the books with a reputation for eroticism, such as *Madame Bovary* and *Lolita* but found them boring. Page after page of unexciting description led only to more descriptive detail of the wallpaper. *Forever Amber* had been banned in Boston and therefore was not expected to make an appearance in our small, provincial village, but I kept looking for it anyway. The tattered, well-read paperbacks scattered around the fo'castle of the *Stanley* had action and raw, red-blooded sex on every eight or ten pages.

Her alabaster thighs glistened in the moonlight as she stepped from the shower smelling like a moist, fecund flower in full blossom. Elaine saw him standing there, waiting. She casually removed the large, white towel, letting it fall...

Rolly, Troy and especially Eddie teased me about the amount of time I spent at the library. Eddie said "Skip, just walk in and ask them for the hottest book they've got–tell them it's for your old Uncle Ed." One afternoon after the *Stanley* docked, I skipped a bath and a change of clothes in order to get to the library before it closed. I thought I could run in and out before anyone noticed.

As usual, an old man in a white shirt and striped tie dozed over the *Wall Street Journal.* The soporific late evening sun streamed through the large windows and dust motes floated in the golden light. I selected several books and counted on a speedy check out, but one of the younger librarians stopped me. Pretty in a plain, shy sort of way, she often wore a soft white sweater that buttoned down the back showing off her young breasts in perfect profile. I also noticed that she left the top two buttons undone, which I interpreted to mean she would enjoy having someone unbutton the rest, all part of my overactive fantasy life. She was at least four years older, out of school and working full time.

Greeting me with a smile, she reached under the massive wooden desk and pulled out a *Horatio Hornblower* novel. "Skip, I kept this out for you. I know you'll like it, it's full of swashbuckling sailor stuff and gory naval battles."

I started to thank her and then noticed a look cross her face; she handed me the book and took a step back. My cheeks burned. Ripe in the warm, bookish air I vowed to never, under any circumstances, ever leave my house without at least one bath!

"Besides all of our paperbacks, what do you like to read, Skip, fiction or nonfiction?" Frank's voice interrupted my uneasy memory, as he threw the contents of his bunk over the wheelhouse deck searching for an elusive ten-amp fuse.

"Mostly nonfiction. But in school I have an English class that I really like."

He interrupted his search and listened intently; he always attended to my comments about school with great interest. "What did you like best about the class?"

"The teacher, Mr. Gault, just got out of the Navy. He's really young, not like the other teachers, and has us read books like *The Ancient Mariner* and *Moby Dick.*"

Frank grinned. His own dog-eared copy of *The Ancient Mariner* fought for space in the wheelhouse bunk and had so far avoided being pitched overboard to make room for more fishing gear. "Schools need more teachers like that. Closer to the kids' age." He gave up the search and pitched everything back in the bunk. "The function of good fiction is to illuminate the truth. The object of first class writing is to edify and help us understand this screwed up world we live in. These imaginary worlds allow us to comprehend the realities of our lives. This is true of all great literature, whether it's science fiction, mystery, adventure, or any other form of fiction. The test of its value is, did I learn anything, do I know more about myself or my environment?"

"The only thing missing is a class on skin books. Maybe you ought to teach one," I suggested. He laughed, but I was only half kidding. I'd learned more from Frank in five minutes than I learned in five months at school.

My interest in reading had intensified the previous summer when I helped a crewmember of the *Frances Elizabeth* do the grocery shopping for the week. Hompie DeCosta, Uncle Hompie to me, could buy most of the items without reading – zucchini is zucchini and chourico is obvious. However, there were items that remained a mystery to him, like Campbell's soups. There were no pictures on the label and Hompie had to read to know the difference between Chicken And Rice and Cream Of Tomato.

My math skills were never great but they were better than Uncle Hompie's. The cost of each individual purchase was written on a brown paper shopping bag and added up by hand. Usually this list extended for the entire length of the bag and occasionally over to a second. My job was to check the math and make sure the list was complete. Five men working 16 to 18 hours a day require an immense amount of food, and by the second time I went with Hompie I decided there was no need to double-check the long list of figures because if there was a slight overcharge one week, sooner or later the law of averages would kick in and there would be a slight undercharge to compensate for any honest errors from the previous purchases.

Grocery shopping always included buying cigarettes for a fishing boat and was considered an essential part of our provisions. Most boats buy one brand, so I became partial to Lucky Strikes. Indeed, running out of cigarettes is a serious event and holds consequences far more compelling than running out of lettuce, milk, or Wheaties. Food, including cigarettes, ice and fuel are always subtracted from the gross income before the shares are divided to pay the crew. I realized I was paying for the cigarettes, so I started smoking between one and one and a half packs a day. They seemed almost free.

Frank wasn't a true chain smoker but he came close. Late one evening, after a long day, I opened the wheelhouse door to give Frank a break and gagged on a god-awful smell. Frank recognized the shock on my face.

"It's alright Skip. Lost all the nerves when I ground off these fingers at the Fore River Ship Yard. Sometimes these damn butts burn down too close and I can't feel it. Mmm, fresh air feels good."

"Sure you're okay?"

"Yeah, it's one of the few benefits, can't feel a thing. A bunch of us were racing–fifty bucks to the winner–trying to see who could grind the most rivets. I was so far ahead I started to show off. When I lost these fingers I was so pissed that I ran 50 yards to the end of the pier just to dump the rest of the rivets, bucket and all, in the water. So stupid, I just wasn't paying attention. But then, I wasn't the only one to leave body parts at the shipyard. There were a lot of guys doing crazy things and somebody was always at sick bay having this or that put back together."

"Did you win the bet?"

"Good guys, truly decent. They all paid me before I got stitched up." He got serious. "You should quit smoking now, before it gets really hard to do."

With the *Louise* tied up on her mooring opposite Plymouth Rock, I would hear the college bound kids giving their talk about the history of Plymouth. Usually I felt sorry for them. They were dressed in heavy, hot Pilgrim garb and forced to pass their hats for whatever income they earned. "We guides receive no compensation other than the generosity of the public." On the *Louise,* I also depended on passing the hat for the majority of my take home pay, the difference being that 90 percent of the time some member of the party did the passing.

Although Plymouth Rock is perhaps the best-known rock in the world, visitors are usually disappointed when they see it. The Pilgrim guides pointed out that only one third of the rock remains, but even my marginal math figured it to be closer to one fifth. It was politically embarrassing for officials to admit that so much of the rock had been damaged or lost. The town decided to move the rock in 1774. Bolts installed to facilitate the process split the rock in two equal pieces. In 1834 during a Fourth of July parade, there was another accident and the rock split again. By 1880, the town cemented the two halves back together but so much was missing that the two pieces no longer matched.

Parts of the rock are now all over the world in the form of paperweights, tie tacks, earrings, and on one occasion, a gift to President Eisenhower. Bits of the rock are also in the Smithsonian and in a concrete floor. Then there are the discarded reminders of summer vacations, little chunks that have either risen to the attic or settled into some dusty corner of the cellar.

During my second week on the *Stanley*, I remembered how accurate Eddie's warning was, that steaking whiting was *really* boring. Frank, possibly sensing our decreasing interest, climbed up into the orange dory that served as our lifeboat. He looked a little like Captain Ahab as he stood in the bow reciting D. H. Lawrence's *Transmitters* and Phyllis McGinley's *A Choice of Weapons*. He mixed in a little swearing, and moved on to *Sharing Eve's Apple* by John Keats. For the last stanza, he raised his voice to a moaning falsetto:

There's a sigh for yes, and a sigh for no,
And a sigh for "I can't bear it!"
Oh what can be done, shall we stay or run?
Oh cut the sweet apple and share it.

Suddenly he screamed, "Jesuuuuus! Jesus suffering Christ! Skip, Skip, for God's sake, what the hell are you doing?"

CARVER PUBLIC LIBRARY

There was a second or two of silence except for the *thump! thump!* as he leaped from the dory to the wheelhouse roof, to the deck, and then lunged at me. Everyone stopped cutting and stared.

"What!" I shouted in alarm.

He yanked up my left hand. The thumb of my glove was gone, neatly severed. "You cut off your Goddamn thumb!"

I waited for the pain and blood, but... nothing. My thumb, safe and sound, popped out of the hole. Relief flooded me. "I'm okay Frank, really!"

He let out a deep breath and released my hand. "You are a lucky son of a bitch!"

My shock retreated, replaced by admiration, then gratitude. Leave it to Frank to spot that piece of glove go overboard with the head of an extra fat whiting! His vision was keen, and I never felt so well watched over. "Wow." As I looked down at the glove with no thumb, the full impact of the near disaster sunk in, and my knees began to shake.

"Here." Eddie passed me a brand new pair of gloves.

"You okay?" Rolly asked, looking me over. "Need to take a break?"

I shook my head and we went back to chopping heads. What I knew, and what Frank knew, was that I'd been going too fast; like him, showing off, going for speed instead of caution. For the next several days I concentrated on safety. And many times I caught myself looking at my left thumb and admiring its beauty.

Mal de Mer

I love the seven seas
Except for when my head is between my knees.

Eileen Quinn, *I love Sailing*

I knew what the sinister-looking five-alarm sunrise meant and glanced at Frank.

"No green flash today, Skip, too damn cloudy."

"Yeah," I said, but my eyes scanned the darkness anyway, and so did his. We had an on-going contest to see who would be first to spot the light that blinked for a split second just before sunrise. Seeing it required perfect weather conditions along with serious concentration.

"The wind's going to ten or fifteen knots and will settle in the northeast," he went on. "By the end of our first tow it'll be raining. By ten we'll all be drenched."

"My grandmother told me to get used to playing in the rain, but I don't think this is what she had in mind," I said with a sigh. Rough weather meant attaching ourselves to the cutting box with rubber belts secured by metal hooks. Scoop up a full box of fish, hook in the left side, pass the rubber belt behind, hook the right side, and begin cutting heads. The deck would be dangerously slick.

Frank nodded. "We'll earn our pay today."

"If this is what it's like raining in mid-June, what's it like snowing in January?" I asked.

"Not as nice as sitting in a warm little schoolhouse surrounded by beautiful young girls. You might not care much for that old maid trying to teach you algebra but she isn't going to get you out of bed at 2:00 in the morning to gut codfish in the snow."

The wind picked up another notch and as the rain grew fiercer, visibility diminished and we lost sight of other boats in the area. We pulled large rubber bands cut from old inner tubes over our boots and bound the bottoms of our oilskins to keep water from filling our knee boots, and settled into the work.

Bad weather on the *Louise* was a different story! Clear the dock as fast as possible, get everyone in the enclosed cabin or under the roof of the fishing deck, and try to keep them happy until we put the anchor down. Passengers didn't have to pay if we never left the dock. However, if we caught even a few fish before heading back in, the skipper could justifiably say that he had purchased gas and bait and therefore deserved to be paid. After all, it was usually the passengers who asked to go in early, not the captain. Charlie's motto was "Take 'em out, get 'em sick, take their money, bring 'em in!" because the earlier we headed in, the less vomit we'd have to mop up.

Seasickness is like having a really bad stomach virus while you're riding a roller coaster. People suffering from *mal de mer* frequently, desperately, offered to pay us to stop fishing early. One particularly bad day we had a woman who was green around the gills by the black and white turn buoy, and violently ill by the Bug Light. She begged Charlie to take her back to the wharf. Patiently he explained that we had 15 other healthy, paying, customers, but reason and logic were no cure. I offered the standard treatment: Saltines eaten slowly while focusing on the horizon. She eyed them unhappily and I had to admit after ten days they hadn't fared well. Soggy, with a touch of mold. In my opinion, they never made anyone feel better except the gulls.

"Wonder if she's sick from the bus ride here?" I asked Charlie quietly.

"Doubt it. She came all the way from Ohio."

Motion sickness is motion sickness. It doesn't make any difference whether you're in an airplane, automobile, ferris wheel or boat. It's all the same–little hairs swishing back and forth inside the middle ear. We passed Saquish and she was crying. Before we reached the Gurnet she promised us a week's pay to return to the pier. Her careful coiffure lay matted over her face. The expensive clothes, much too nice for fishing, were rumpled, twisted and stained green with partially digested food.

Charlie compromised by agreeing to fish inside the Gurnet. Silent, sympathetic, the rest of the passengers watched our slow, unsteady progress as I helped her down into the cabin. Another passenger claiming to have nursing experience took pity on her, but only made the situation worse by pressing a damp rag stinking of fish to her forehead.

"You'll feel better soon," I said, knowing this would not happen until she felt the solid earth under her feet. In the dark cabin she was so pale that she glowed eerily, her hair and face shades of light blue. I turned to the nurse. "How's her pulse?"

"Racing, She needs to take deep breaths."

The woman rolled over and heaved. By now there was no food left in her stomach to eject, and her struggles were pitiful and ineffective. Still hanging over the edge of the bench, she used up the last of her strength to moan.

I stared directly at the nurse and said, "Maybe she has a weak heart, just like my aunt." The nurse started to shake her head no and then noticed me smiling and nodding yes.

"Ohh!" The nurse nodded too. "I bet you're right. In fact... " she took another look and declared, "This woman isn't seasick. She's having a heart attack!"

"Yes," I said, "I believe it might be."

"*Heart attack*?" The woman struggled to sit up.

The nurse took her hand. "Heart attack," she confirmed. "Which means we have to get you back to shore right away!"

"Ohhh..." the woman's eyes filled with indescribable relief and she lay back again.

"Go tell your captain," the nurse said. "Or would you rather I do it?"

"Well, you're the nurse," I said.

We arrived at the dock in less than an hour.

As if reading my mind, Frank leaned out the wheelhouse window and shouted, "Hey, Skip, not a single party boat out here today!"

"No shit!" On the worst days most of the customers on the *Louise* would be eager to leave early, but we usually had one or two who insisted on getting their money's worth, and we'd finish out the afternoon. People would throw up everywhere except in the toilet or over the rail. Sometimes a sick customer would "accidentally" vomit on the lunch, camera and extra clothing of those who insisted on staying, giving them a rich coating of their last three meals. After a rough day I scrubbed every square millimeter of the cabin several times. If I missed even one small area, the odor would become obnoxious in a day or two.

I was, however, obsessed with finding one type of regurgitation. Whale puke–Ambergris–was used in the production of expensive perfumes, and was worth zillions of dollars per ounce. Find a whale that's sick to its stomach, scoop the stuff up, and retire to a life of opulent leisure. Unfortunately, no one in Plymouth had ever seen any. No one had ever bought a big house and retired. No one, and I mean *no one*, could describe exactly what it looked like. Some said it was a gray, waxy, greasy substance. Others said you would know it when you saw it–just look for really big puddles of puke.

Two years previously I spotted a small right whale hit by a passing tanker or freighter. Clouds of gulls hovering over it made it easy to find. Some had been feasting so long they were unable to fly away as we approached. Fifteen customers hung over the rail to see. It absolutely reeked, the smell almost visible, spiraling up as if in a hurried effort to escape the rotting body.

I grabbed Charlie. "This is our big chance!"

"What the hell you talking about?" He glared at me, preoccupied with steering away. "What big chance?"

"Ambergris! I bet that whale's full of it!"

"Skippy, you want everybody on board to lose their lunch?"

"But..."

"That stench will have me spilling my cookies, never mind everyone else!"

On a boat there's only one boss, and it wasn't me. Unhappily I watched as my dreams of decadent wealth disappeared on the horizon.

The *Stanley* never considered heading in because of a little wet weather, so we put in a full day at the cutting table; raw and wet. When I got home that evening, I climbed into a tub as hot as I could stand it and soaked until the water cooled. Overnight the wind and rain increased. When the alarm went off at 3:00, the wind's whistle and the intensity of the rain on the window assured me it was safe to roll over and go back to sleep; no fishing today. I forced myself to stay awake as long as possible to enjoy the extravagant indulgence of a warm, dry bed and the thrill of telling the alarm clock to go directly to hell. At least for this one morning, it gave me a perverse pleasure to dictate to the clock rather than being its obedient slave.

Troy needed a few days ashore and Frank asked Eddie if he would take over as cook.

"I can't stand the thought of bringing that one-armed guy back," Frank said. "The last trip he made with us, I couldn't eat anything for days thinking about those mashed potatoes."

"What one-armed guy?" I asked.

Frank rolled his eyes. "Guy I know. Lives on a government pension, he's basically unemployed, so he's available on short notice."

"Only reason he got here on time was because someone pushed him out of their car and onto the dock after the last bar closed," Eddie put in. "He was here when I got here, so I sorta nudged him with my foot. Nothing. A bucket of cold salt water did the trick!"

"Woke him so he could stumble on board and pass out again," Frank said. "Slept like a baby until the first tow." He filled another twine needle and tried to keep up with Eddie as we repaired a jagged hole in the net. "He sobered up during the day and started the little black stove to cook dinner. You know how hot the fo'castle gets when the stove is on? Well he strips to the waist and starts to mash potatoes using the stump of his prosthesis."

I laughed, picturing it.

But Frank shook his head. "Sure, funny to you because you weren't there! I come down the ladder and see this big, disgusting, oily drunk dripping sweat into my mashed potatoes."

"Did you eat it?"

"Hell no! I threw it overboard, pot and all."

"Not even the fish would eat it!" Eddie said. "They cleared out as soon as it hit the water."

Frank put his hand on Eddie's shoulder with a hopeful nod. "So you'll cook?"

"Okay, Capt, but just this one trip."

Frank turned to me. "You'll see, Eddie's a great cook. His meals have a distinctive Portuguese flavor." He put his thumb and forefinger together and kissed them like a connoisseur of fine cuisine, "When he cooks, every day is like Thanksgiving."

Eddie's first dish was fish chowder made with codfish cheeks, tongues and the remnants of heads, which simmered for hours.

"I try to scoop out all the eyeballs," he explained as I watched him prepare it, "but I like to maintain the integrity of cooking the entire head. Years ago young boys would start their fishing careers by cutting out tongues, cheeks and cod livers. These were saved separately and sold as high-profit by-products. Cheeks and tongues are delicious, boneless cod delicacies. Livers were used to formulate cod liver oil, one of the first vitamin supplements, and may have been the birth of the pharmaceutical vitamin industry."

"Cod liver oil!" I made a face.

"It's good for you."

"I know. My mother thinks it can cure everything from bed wetting to cancer."

"It's got vitamin D–that prevents rickets. Before cod liver oil, kids used to have to swallow the whole liver." He chuckled as the fo'castle took on the fragrance of an expensive restaurant. "Sometimes fishermen find stuff in the bellies of cod. False teeth, diamond rings, you name it."

"I know, I've heard that. How, though? When I'm gutting cod, I only handle it for a second. Who's got time to search the belly for treasures?"

Frank, coming down the ladder, entered the conversation. "Those are just fables. Poor people, especially those living on islands, used every part of the fish, took the intestines and stuffed them similar to the tripe we eat today. In the process, they examined everything inside the fish." He took a sniff, and nodded, then turned to me. "Did Eddie tell you about his rule?"

"Rule? No. What is it?"

Eddie stirred the pot and delicately tested a spoonful. "The first son of a bitch that complains about my cooking has to take over. No exceptions."

"Sounds good to me. I won't complain unless you run out!" I said.

The next day he marinated roast beef with onions, garlic and red wine beginning early in the morning, and once it was in the oven, everyone began to salivate. One by one we kept popping down to inquire when it would be done. Later in the day he sautéed carrots, boiled fresh green beans and mashed potatoes with extra butter and garlic. At long last, he declared the meal ready and we sat down, ravenous.

Frank served himself a plate piled high with all his favorite food and sat down praising Eddie for his Epicurean expertise, culinary competence, not to mention his gastronomical greatness. With exaggerated elegance he sampled the meat and pronounced it ambrosia. I always got a kick out of the way he was finicky about food. Performing heavy physical labor required a high-calorie diet and the rest of us could, and would, eat anything not nailed down; from Troy's southern cooking of okra, mustard greens and butterbeans to gobs of peanut butter and jelly on toast, or bologna on white bread.

"Eddie, Old Dog, you are the best chef on land or sea," he declared, "I'd eat the ass end off a running skunk if you cooked it. These are the best mother-loving carrots I've ever tasted." Saving the best for last, he reached for the mashed potatoes, poured on a double helping of gravy, preparing to give one of his favorite foods the highest of all compliments. With great care, he slowly took his first mouthful. His expression changed immediately. Tears ran down his cheeks. "My god," he gasped. "These potatoes are salty! Saltier than Lot's wife." In an instant though he remembered Eddie's rule, and amended, "Best I ever had!" Eddie confessed that he had used two full boxes of salt plus secret ingredients to flavor the potatoes. With good-natured admiration of Frank's instant response, Eddie swiftly reached down to one of the larger cupboards, and pulled out a huge pot of steaming, undoctored potatoes. Everyone laughed, Eddie most of all. The rest of us were thankful that it had been Frank who was the first to test the food.

By July whiting were plentiful, and prices dropped.

"Just consider it," I heard Eddie say to Frank one morning.

"Consider what?" I asked.

"Eddie wants to quit steaking whiting and try ground fishing for cod, haddock and flounder," Frank said.

Eddie held out his hands, and his wrists, like mine, like everyone's on board, were covered with the gurry sores incurred after long hours of skin being chafed by the cotton gloves. "Have mercy," he said.

Frank looked out over the water. I knew he was thinking, weighing the pros and cons; considering the odds of success. This was not a decision to be made lightly, with the livelihood of five people, some with families, depending on the outcome. "Okay," he said. "The price of codfish isn't that great either, but let's try it."

I vibrated with enthusiasm. No more chopping heads! No more long, monotonous hours spent hunched over a box of whiting! Frank, observing my excitement, said, "Before you start ringing bells, wait and see what tomorrow brings."

Our initial trip proved typical for ground fishing. The first several tows produced small amounts of cod and black-back flounders. We cleared the deck, iced down the fish and had half an hour to relax. I did an enormous arms over the head stretch and said, "This is beautiful, what a great way to fish!"

"Yeah, and a lousy way to make money," Troy said. "We haven't even paid for your food, much less the diesel fuel."

Frank, Eddie, and Rolly conferred after every tow and gradually we moved off the thirty-fathom line to the forty and then to the forty-five. By 10:00 that night we had to split the bag because the net overflowed with medium to large codfish. We quickly re-set the net, placed a buoy at the northern edge of the tow to help us avoid running into the rock piles, and started to gut codfish.

Standing knee deep in large cod, Eddie picked up a fat twenty-pound fish, jumped up on the hatch covers, and danced with this beauty as he sang one of his favorite songs:

The girls of Gloucester have no combs
They comb their hair with codfish bones.

Frank called out from the pilothouse, "Give her a big wet French kiss for me!" and Eddie gave the cod a lingering, theatrical smack, licked his lips with satisfaction, and added the privileged beauty to our growing pile of processed fish.

At daybreak Frank started to bring the boat around broadside to the wind. We still had fish to ice down. We were making money now and the leisure time of the morning seemed as remote as Mongolia.

"Price of cod is the highest it's been since April," Frank said. "If we keep going we should have a full trip by noon tomorrow. What do you guys want to do, keep everyone on deck or start regular watches?"

"This fishing's too good to lose one man to sleep, so let's just go with mug ups until morning," Eddie said. "Then we can decide how many more fish we need."

An accepted standard for any crew working several consecutive days was eight hours on duty and four hours off, so in theory everyone got eight hours of sleep every twenty-four hours. In reality you needed to get below on time, have something to eat, jump in the rack, and try to snag three uninterrupted hours. One of my many heroes, Thomas Edison, lived most of his adult life on just a few hours of sleep each night, supplemented with short catnaps during the day. I envied Edison this ability, and reasoned that thinking couldn't be that much harder than physical labor.

Overriding all theory was the real rule: fill the fish hold as quickly as possible and make it back to port using the least amount of food and fuel possible.

At 6:00 a.m. Frank leaned out the wheelhouse window and yelled, "The price is still up, none of the big beam trawlers unloaded in Gloucester or New Bedford. Let's work until 8:00, eat breakfast and fish until we can't fit another cod in the hold."

At 7:30 Troy went down to prepare breakfast. We followed him half an hour later, groaning and rubbing aching backs. Relaxing for the first time in 26 hours; weary but not tired. Knowing our first ground-fishing trip was a huge success put everyone in a slaphappy mood and we joked about how we would spend our anticipated wealth.

Troy, exhausted like the rest of us, cooked a gigantic amount of eggs, bacon, fried fish and toast, but he participated in the giddy conversation–*Gonna buy my wife a Cadillac!* while accidentally overcooking the eggs. "Shit, I ruined 'em! They'll be tougher than hell."

"I'm sure they're fine." Starved, Eddie reached for one. He took a bite and we laughed at his efforts to chew. "These aren't eggs!" he said, holding the unyielding yoke between his teeth, the whites flapping on either side of his mouth, "They're skate wings!" In one courageous gulp, he swallowed it. If he could eat the eggs, so could we, and we fell in.

"Christ!" shouted Frank, "I got boots softer than this!"

I had just crammed my mouth full of bacon, toast and heat-hardened eggs, and his remark struck me as so funny that I laughed, gasped and sucked in a breath. I started to say something, and then realized I couldn't breathe. Couldn't breathe! I couldn't force one single molecule of air into my lungs! The skate wings were about to take their revenge and my young life was going to end here in the fo'castle of a fishing boat, miles away from friends and family. How would they explain my untimely demise? Was I going to die before I made love to a woman?

About to pass out from lack of oxygen, I felt myself being lifted up. Light, feathery, I floated higher. In my hazy, airless state, I wondered if an angel was pulling me up to heaven. WHOOOMPH!!! A large, hard fist landed squarely in the center of my upper abdomen. SPLAT. A wad blasted out of my mouth, stuck to the wall, and suddenly I could breathe! Hallelujah! Praise the Lord! I'll never sin again–ever!

Eddie's right hand was still balled in the fist that had saved my life. My angel of mercy wore knee boots, a plaid shirt stained with sweat and cod guts and a three-day-old-beard. He smelled worse than the cod, but he was my first glimpse of the savior. "You okay, Skip?"

I nodded, but couldn't speak yet.

Your life passes in front of you as you're about to die," Frank said, almost as shaken up as me. He put his hand on my arm, watching carefully as I took another deep breath. "Once I was working on top of the Sagamore Bridge at the east end of the Canal and I lost my footing. As I fell, I saw something like a movie of my life; high school, boxing, Army, prison, the shipyard. A real mystical experience! The movie stopped and I found myself swinging in a God-awful, nerve-shattering arc. I stared down hundreds of feet at the rocks and water below through large rope meshes of a safety net, just like a trapped codfish. I have no idea how I crawled out of the net. Probably scared the shit outa the crew!"

I nodded again. With his hand still on my arm, I felt, more than heard, what he was communicating to me.

When we reached the dock, the price of cod had dropped slightly but still hovered at nearly twice the price of whiting. Furthermore, we had the same amount of cod as we would have had in whiting. Frank asked us to wait for him to settle up with the buyer. We were in the fo'castle when he bounced down the ladder.

"Look at this, ladies! How's it feel to be richer than Rockefeller, wealthier than old Daddy Warbucks? Look!" He reached in his pocket, pulled out a wad of bills, and threw them in the air. Ten and twenty dollar bills floated into eager fists as we grabbed and snatched and laughed.

"How much is here, Capt?" Rolly asked, fetching two twenties from under the table.

"More than we'd get steaking whiting, that's for sure," Frank replied. "We'll need the armored car to take us to the bank!"

As I leaned down to pick up one more twenty, I felt a sharp pain. The ache in my ribs from Eddie's punch lasted for two weeks, but served as a somber reminder of something that I had taken for granted, but never would again.

Nights In Provincetown

No man is an island, entire of itself;
every man is a piece of the continent, a part of the main.
If a clod be washed away by the sea,
Europe is the less, as well as if a promontory were,
as well as if a manor of thy friends or of thine own were.
Any man's death diminishes me, because I am involved in mankind;
and therefore never send to know for whom the bell tolls;
it tolls for thee...

John Donne, *No Man is an Island*

If Frank's favorite place to stand was in our dory / lifeboat, mine was at the top of our 25-foot mast. Best view in the house! The four-foot mast on the *Louise* functioned strictly as an ornament, so it was Eddie who taught me how to climb.

"Always climb on the inboard roll," he said. "The inward pressure will keep you close to the ladder. Rest and just hang on while the boat rolls outboard. You want both hands and feet firmly on the ladder when the boat moves you out, over the water." Standing on deck, he held the second wooden crossbar, muscles rippling in his forearm. "When you're climbing, your feet are on the crossbars, but keep your hands on the upright metal cables fastened to the cross tree. These wooden rungs are lashed onto the vertical cables with mending twine. If the twine slips or breaks, you want your hands on something solid. Remember, most people only fall once. I don't want to pick up pieces of you off the deck."

It surprised me how much the motion on deck was magnified at the height of the mast. The thrill rides at Nantasket Beach couldn't compare to this! Swaying high above the undulating currents of tuna, mackerel and bluefish felt compelling, seductive. The shallow sand bars changed from bright yellow to deep purple as the depth increased and this was all the art appreciation I needed. At the top of the mast, I was king of the mountain, ruler of all I surveyed. Far above the common labor of cleaning cod and shoveling trash fish.

"Unchained to the rock, and unfettered to the soil," Frank greeted me as I climbed back down on deck. "Think Columbus felt the same way as he climbed to the top of his mast? Did his eagerness to sight land, any land, outweigh yours?"

"No, Capt, he had too much on his mind to enjoy it the way I do. Pictures I've seen of the *Santa Maria* show her main mast taller than I expected."

"Our masts are very different in function, ours will never hold a sail, only heavy loads of fish or scallops. One of the few records of the *Santa Maria* shows her as drawing approximately the same amount of water as the *Stanley*. By extension, she might have carried a mast slightly taller than ours, at least that's the way I like to think of her." He turned off the blaring radio. "The real question is, when Columbus climbed to the top of his mast, did he think about the curve of the earth, his view unimpeded by hills and forests, did he think he saw India or China?"

"I'm not sure." A pair of gannets skimming the water caught my attention. With a body three feet long and a wing span close to six feet, gannets are built with a single purpose–diving. Circling 30 to 50 feet above their prey, they power dive straight into the water spewing a geyser six to eight feet in the air. The effect of a flock of gannets diving from fifty feet is the same as dropping frozen turkeys from that height–unforgettable. The precisely painted black tips on the glistening white wings add to the illusion of a dive-bomber; their yellow head, a royal crown. Although gannets move up and down the coast during their spring and fall migrations, they summer at their breeding grounds on Bonadventure Island, near the Gaspe' Peninsula. "A bit early in the year for them, isn't it?"

"A bit," Frank agreed. "They're either the horniest gannets in the world and just couldn't wait until they got up north; or the least motivated to procreate, and just said the hell with it, let's stop right here."

"I'm with the gannets," Eddie spoke up. "Stay here, away from the sharp claws of women."

Frank and I laughed sympathetically. Eddie's marriage was on the rocks.

"If I lived here I wouldn't have to deal with my dad," I said. The confession startled me, it had just popped out. My father's drinking was something I didn't talk about much; enough of the neighbors knew from having seen and heard him. Since Frank lived just a few houses away, I assumed he knew, but he had never said anything.

In silence we watched the gannets dip and dive. Finally Frank said,

"The solution is obvious. We live here. With a few beautiful women. But the women don't speak any English."

"And they do all the cooking," Troy said.

"And know how to fix the engine if it breaks down," Rolly added.

We joked and shoved each other, men who'd seen it all. For a few minutes, I was one of them.

Early in July Frank suggested we take a break from Plymouth and head for Provincetown. On the way he pointed out Pilgrim Monument.

"Three hundred forty-eight feet above the horizon," he said. "If ever a town deserves a phallic symbol, it's P'town. It exists in a world of its own at the end of the Cape; sometimes it feels like the end of the world. One major street, long and slender, contains a worldview as wide as all humanity. Ever been?"

"No. Heard about it, but never been."

"It's crowded and noisy in summer, lonely and deserted in the winter, and embraces these changes as naturally as the seasons. More so than Gloucester, New Bedford or Boston. It's the fishiest town on the East Coast. Other ports land greater quantities but they encompass other industries."

"If they depend on fishing and tourists all summer, how do they survive the winters?" I asked.

"Just fishing, Skip, just fishing." Frank paused to chugalug a bottle of Coca Cola. "From the earliest days, the town's name has been synonymous with fish. Early in the 1600s, explorers like Gosnold and Champlain remarked on the teeming shoals of fish in the area. Gosnold wrote in his journal *It's a harbor large enough to anchor a thousand ships, and we took a great store of ye cod-fishies..*

"Huh," I said. It always amazed me that he could just quote stuff.

"Late in the 1600s," Frank went on, unmindful of my admiration, "it harbored a population of fishermen, smugglers, outlaws, escaped indentured servants, heavy drinkers; a lawless, frontier-like scene. Often called Helltown, it embarrassed its neighbors in Truro and easily lived up to its reputation. Probably still does."

"I can't wait to see it," I said.

It felt like forever, but eventually we tied up at MacMillan Wharf alongside two other local draggers, the *CR&M* and the *Shirley* and *Roland*. Day boats that went to Stellwagen Bank or around to the backside of Cape Cod, then returned to port each evening. Most of the crew were Portuguese, whose ability to steak whiting earned our respect. Some called this Portuguese Power or "pusha, pusha"–push those heads off the cutting board and keep one in the air all day long. Not easy work in light of the fact that "all day" meant fourteen to sixteen hours.

Frank stepped out on deck. "Everybody claims that these Provincetown boats catch more fish than we do and there is one reason why. Just look at those guys, truly ancient mariners, stopping no one, sitting around smoking stogies or cigarillos and waiting for the next torn net. If a Provincetown boat damages a net, all the skipper does is change to a spare and haul the damaged gear onto the pier, knowing it will be perfectly mended by the next day. We should be that lucky."

Eddie looked up at a newly patched net. "My God, Capt., it's a beautiful sight! If we put into Gloucester, my uncles would mend twine for us. The problem is none of us have any old goat relatives in Plymouth."

Frank explained, "Most of the net menders are family members of the crews, so they mend nets in exchange for a couple of lobsters or a few choice haddock fillets. Like Eddie, they started mending nets before they turned ten."

"While you were still in diapers, Skip," Eddie said.

"Very funny." I punched his arm and he made a face and rubbed it; like I was so strong that it hurt a lot. "So what are they fishing for?"

"Anything that swims by–tinker mackerel, tommy cod, " Frank said. "These guys have been fishing since they were 12 or 13. See all the missing teeth?"

I nodded. Not just the dental dilemmas, but bent, withered or amputated body parts. I would love to have asked about their largest cod, the worst storm, the things they missed most; but they seemed more comfortable with their own company.

As the Boston to Provincetown steamer eased slowly away from the dock, a group of teenagers swam around her. Passengers on the top deck threw quarters and sometimes half dollars to watch the boys dive for them. The divers looked like well-bronzed seals frolicking in the clear, shallow water. They were powerful, natural swimmers, totally at home in Provincetown's natural community pool. Out of water their dark hair, smoothed over their heads, matched the soft brown fuzz on their backs.

"Watch carefully," Frank said. "Those shiny coins will saucer down until a boy snatches it up, or until it sinks out of sight. Sometimes when a quarter drops too fast, and the swimmer can't grab it, he'll reach into his mouth, pull out a previously caught coin, and race to the surface to reassure the crowd that their coins are not wasted."

This game required one level of skill while the boat remained tied to the dock, but more finesse was required when she started to get under way. Now the swimmers had to stay within range of the money and avoid getting too close to the propellers. Visitors and swimmers both enjoyed the sport. It reminded me of times I'd tossed shiny round lures to a school of fast fish–large, quick and intelligent, they fed only on sunny days for short periods of time and were very selective about their food. The round silver lures (coins) failed at night; more exotic bait, like young women, pizza and beer was required to attract the young men after dark.

"Have you read any of Ben Franklin's writings?" Frank asked. Inhaling deeply from a new cigarette, a cloud of blue smoke swirled around his face. When I shook my head, he wrinkled his nose as if I had some contagious disease. "Skip, you really should read more of the classics. You can learn so much from them."

"I know." Waiting for him to go on, all I could think was that someone so refined belonged up on that boat, drinking perfect martinis and chatting with beautiful women. I wondered if he felt that way too, which made me sad; but at the same time, I was willing to bet no one on that boat was talking about Ben Franklin.

"He proposed a method for learning how to swim: walk into the water until you're chest deep, turn around until you face the shore, and throw an egg into the water. It must be deep enough so you cannot reach it without diving. Now try diving towards the egg."

"Uh huh."

"The water buoys you up unless you actively try to dive under. It's not so easy to sink as you imagine, and really hard work to get down to the egg. You feel the power of the water supporting you, and learn confidence in that power while you try to overcome it. It also teaches you how to use your hands and feet, and then all you need is to hold your head out of the water."

"I know how to swim," I reminded him, "but maybe we should teach Eddie."

"Believe me, I've tried. He resists."

"Is he scared?"

""No, not at all, he simply doesn't see the value to it–sort of like you and going to school." Frank continued to stare at the steamer as it slid into the bright afternoon sun. Its intense glare reflected off the water, causing us both to squint. "Franklin is the perfect example of a man who thought deeply about our world. A true renaissance man. Nothing was too low or too high for his serious consideration. He tells a story about a Presbyterian minister who complained that men did not attend his sermons and prayers. He said, *It is perhaps below the dignity of your profession to act as the steward of the rum, but if you were to deal it out, and only just after prayers, you would have them all about you.*"

"They probably wanted prayers three times a day from that point on," I laughed. "Actually I do remember something Franklin said: *Too much religion is worse than not enough.* I tried to use that line on my mother."

"How'd it work?"

"I still wound up in church every Sunday." My nose caught the fragrance of the waterfront; sea air and fish blended with the odors of local restaurants. The rich chocolate aroma of fudge mingled with fried clams seemed to invite us into town to sample its diverse flavors. "Wow, I'm getting hungry!"

"If you ever want to operate a successful restaurant, you must have the smell of onions to draw people into the place," Frank chuckled. "It's the same with the vendors out here on the pier. No one can resist the aroma of sautéed onions. The formula for running a profitable restaurant is pretty straightforward: Have good help, delicious food and a fair price. The hardest part is attracting customers."

Troy smacked my arm. "No trouble getting this kid in."

The others laughed. I took a lot of ribbing about my appetite, which was bigger than anyone else's. In fact, once the three or four-day trips began, Troy noticed that ice cream, pies and entire cakes were simply disappearing on the first day. Since I ate after everyone else had finished, the culprit was easily flushed out and Troy started hiding food from me. But his system of food concealment harbored a serious flaw: he often forgot where he hid stuff. Sometimes I would see him searching for goodies like a frustrated squirrel. If I had eaten it in the recent past, I 'fessed up. But usually someone would stumble across it weeks later, blue-green with mold. It killed me to watch him throw food overboard.

The *Frances Elizabeth* headed in to dock. The whiting boats didn't fish on Friday and Saturday because the New York buyers were closed. The *Frances Elizabeth* did not steak whiting but simply bailed them, heads and all, in large wooden barrels, iced them down and unloaded their catch Sunday through Thursday in Plymouth. Her captain, Jack Rivers, "Captain Jack," had been born Joaquim Revez in a small village in Portugal. When he arrived at Ellis Island around 1913, the name became anglicized to its current WASP equivalent. His boat usually carried four crewmembers, including Captain Jack's sons Jackie and Louie (Louie was ten years older than me and had been class president and valedictorian.), Antonio Andrè, and Joe Correa, known affectionately as Joe Cow. The Portuguese love nicknames and use them to distinguish one from the other; there are so many named Joe, John or Maria; Costa, Souza, Cabral or Roderick. Also, not having a nickname implies you come from a very poor Anglo family and no one cares enough to give you another name. While there were nicknames in Plymouth, they paled by comparison. The Provincetowners carry names for life – Squiddy, Bunny, Whitey, Blondie, Jessie James, Moony, Doc, Didda, Spike, Peachy, Hompie, Perry, Cousin, Khaki, Colonel Fernel, Lovie, Bubba, Corny and on and on.

"Most of New England's whiting goes to New York to make Jewish gefilte-fish. Our buyer, Reliable Fish, offers contracts or guarantees to buy a predetermined amount of fish. Could be a big attraction to Captain Jack," Frank said.

Whatever the reason, it felt good to see familiar faces coming into the pier.

On the *Stanley* we planned to have a quick supper and hit the town. Making ourselves presentable, however, was a challenge. My recent embarrassment at the Plymouth Library still caused me to blush, and I became compulsive about my evening toilette. The *Stanley*'s lavatory amenities consisted of hanging our buns off the stern in good weather or alternatively using an old five-gallon Esso oil can. A real fresh water shower never entered our minds. We took turns stripping to our skivvies and hosing each other down with the large salt-water deck hose. Our choices consisted of feeling the scratchy salt or a facecloth wash, sometimes called a French bath. Although I had not yet started to shave, I applied a triple dose of Eddie's Old Spice aftershave lotion, hoping it would confound the senses enough to minimize the ever-present aroma of codfish, all the while wishing I had some Secret Love Musk. I'd seen ads in comic books, *The Police Gazette* and other men's publications for this magical potion that could reduce women into pools of panting desire, begging to have their clothes ripped off. Apparently through the marvels of chemistry, scientists had formulated extracts from animals in heat and applied these principles to humans. No woman could resist fulfilling a man's every wish. Unfortunately no one on board had any.

We arrived on Commercial Street before dark, feeling like five Musketeers. The tourists gawked at us and we ogled them back. Seeing two especially attractive young women, one of them exceptionally well endowed, Eddie called out "Varoom, Varoom!"

"Heads up, Old Dogs, here comes the whole desirable dairy," Frank said.

"Lawdey, what bazongas!" Troy said, with a look halfway between innocence and lecher.

"Mmm, nice set of twins," Rolly said.

"They don't even look like sisters to me," I replied.

Rolly laughed. "No, twin headlights."

Indeed, the girls literally stood out in the crowd because they wanted to, and I noticed every male, regardless of age or persuasion, felt compelled to look. We continued on to Wuthering Heights, one of many local clubs, and walked in just as the first show began.

The waiter's face lit up when he saw Frank, and he hurried over, beaming. "Captain Frank! Welcome back, it's always good to see you and your friends. Thanks for choosing my table this evening."

"It's good to be back, Bobbie. Five drafts, please." When Bobbie gave me a questioning look, Frank explained, "He's with us." Bobbie nodded, satisfied with the explanation.

The Master of Ceremonies told a few old, tired jokes: "Good evening Ladies and... what? There are no ladies here? Good, because there aren't any gentlemen either! Ha ha ha! Welcome, Welcome Jelly Beans and all you drag queens, lubricated up with extra Vaseline! Quick! What's the difference between a new wife and a new dog? After a year, the dog is still excited to see you! Ha ha ha. How is a married man and a fisherman alike? They both complain about the one they caught and brag about the one that got away."

The audience laughed, not because the jokes were funny, but because they were drinking and cheerful. Some heckled the MC, but it was all in good fun, and he blew them kisses. "And now," he went on, "all you lovers of the lascivious; all you with lecherous libidos, please give a sultry, summer welcome to the Bell of Gaytonia, Bella Bayyyonaaaa!"

Bella Bayona turned out to be a short, stocky, middle-aged man dressed in a shiny, black jock strap, swaying back and forth on a swing suspended from the ceiling and lowered slowly to the stage. He slid gracefully off the perch, his body glistening with oil and draped with wide-mesh fish net. In his left hand he held a home-made trident, à la Neptune. "This first number is dedicated to the brave and intrepid fishermen of the *J. L. Stanley and Sons*–they that sail upon the wine dark sea."

Embarrassed, I scrunched up my shoulders with face burning, just knowing everyone in the place was looking at us, wondering how we knew such a freak! But as he began to sing, I found myself, like the rest of the audience, entranced. He had a beautiful baritone voice and an unexpected agility, and he'd composed a song for us! It was unbelievable, inconceivable, that someone would publicly recognize a bunch of insignificant, smelly fishermen, one of whom was still in his rolled down rubber boots. Accompanied by drums, piano, and bass combo, Bella sang and danced,

They've all been paid and need to be laid,
Frank's fond of brown eyes and muscular thighs,
Oh, look what I've found; while playing around!

Soon the entire club was stomping to keep time, pounding on the floor and beating on the table.

"This is the song of life," Frank shouted into my ear. "This is the poetry of living. Savor it all, enjoy every morsel."

When his performance ended amidst boisterous cheers, Bella let the mesh net drop (more shouting) issued a teasing grin, then pulled on a silk bathrobe, an enormous hat and headed for our table. Frank stood and greeted him with a handshake while Eddie pulled over another chair.

"Skip," said Frank, "say hello to my good friend Phil. He owns this bar."

Phil beamed. "Darling! You must be new with Frank. A very warm welcome to Wuthering Heights."

"Th-thanks," I stuttered. What I really wanted to ask was how could he wear that little jock strap? but it came out as, "Where did you find that ratty old fish net?" God, I felt dim-witted.

"Oh, my friend, Louie Rivers gave it to me."

As if to rescue me from further embarrassment, Varoom and Bazongas walked in. Frank and Phil headed for a direct rendezvous. Bazongas blew the largest bubble of pink gum I'd ever seen. For a few seconds it totally covered her face. Phil welcomed them to his club and Frank, acting as *maitre d'*, invited them to a special, reserved table, one he was sure they would like–ours. Soon we were all enjoying the company, drinking beer as if we had known each other since kindergarten.

Bazonga, whose real name was Natasha, chugalugged her beer and ordered a double shot of *wodka*, downing it in a single gulp.

"So, you're Russian?" Phil asked her.

"My ancestors go back to Alex Michailovich, father of Peter the Great. My uncles and father all died in the var. It is hard leeving here, but is impossible to leeve vis dose bastards in my homeland."

I noticed a large Zorro shaped scar running vertically on the left side of her face. It was obvious, too, that her left arm had been broken, and when it was set, all the pieces didn't line up.

Another double vodka and her story became darker. She was ten or twelve years older than me, and if half of what she said was true, she'd seen far too much killing, rape, torture and starvation. "Josef Stalin, de butcher!" she said. "De son of a syphilis whore; and de blood, de prisons, de churches, de poverty, de slaughter!"

Phil reached over and took her hand; lifted it and tenderly kissed her wrist. Then he said heartily, "Come on, Baby! This is a party, not the last goddamn rites!"

We laughed, and she did too. I saw how much prettier she became once her gloom lifted.

"Skip, what do you think of fishing, do you enjoy it?" Phil inquired.

"It's easier than thinking," I replied.

"Here here!" Frank shouted, lifting his beer. We lifted ours, too, and everyone clinked glasses. No one seemed to pay any attention to the perfectly tanned young men on the other side of the room, holding hands and caressing each other's thighs, so I tried unsuccessfully not to stare. I needed to convince myself that my eyes were not playing tricks, that it wasn't just a girl with a short haircut.

Eddie gave me an obvious nudge and said, "If you want a date, I'll introduce you."

Phil turned to Varoom. "What's brings you to P'town?"

Varoom said her name was Margaret and she told us to call her Maggie. A black choker accentuated her swan neck and narrow shoulders. Her peasant blouse rode low on her shoulders with no bra strap to interrupt the expanse of skin.

"We're working as waitresses in Hyannis and decided to come down here–maybe find a better job."

"You want to go fishing?" Eddie asked.

She gave a playful shove. "Hell, yes, I've tried some of those brainy jobs and they didn't work out so well."

Eddie pulled out a fresh pack of cigarettes, popped up three or four; a savvy, sophisticated gesture. She put her hand on his wrist and slowly, slower than necessary, pulled one out.

"How did you get in this business?" I asked Phil.

"I love voice and ballet, but even as a teenager I never had the build for a male dancer. Actually, a lot of the theater arts are much too somber and serious for me. I love what I do here." He smiled his Buddha smile and I knew why Frank enjoyed his company. "People laugh, joke, have a good time and leave their troubles behind, if only for a short time. Everybody comes in here, year-round residents and tourists, straights and gays, artists and actors, mega rich and poverty poor, poets and pilgrims, iconoclasts and conservatives, students and teachers, fishermen and physicists all come to my place. There's my friend, Louie Rivers, just sitting down over there with a group of his amigos." We both waved, but Louie was engaged with a group of friends.

"Greenwich Village discovered Provincetown as a place where they could escape the suffocation of summer in New York City and not modify their life styles. Like every one else, residents of the Village knew that a change of scenery boosted their creativity. This is my home, my people. Yes, I am the entertainer, but I am also the one who is entertained. I don't know what I would do if I had to get a job, a real job like yours."

None of us could imagine dancing around, dressed in olive oil and mending twine, while singing songs we wrote. I suspected that Phil would never see himself in a full set of oilskins, chopping off fish heads.

Phil reached into his shiny robe pocket and extracted a long, black and gold cigarette holder. Frank offered him a Lucky Strike but he politely refused and produced a Pall Mall. "Better for my voice, especially when I'm doing two shows a night." He lit up elegantly, turned to me. "Skip, are you still in school?"

I hesitated for a fraction of a second. Frank answered, "Bet your ass he is!"

"Good. Lots of kids your age drop out. It's tragic, but I won't hire anyone without a high school diploma."

I nodded. I had to admit, I was enchanted. A light radiated from Phil. His love of humanity saturated the atmosphere. The question regarding school was not casual small talk. I knew he cared deeply about the answer.

"Not Skip," said Frank. "He's not going to drop out."

"You may not realize it yet, young Skip," Phil said, "but Frank is not just your run of the mill ex-con."

"Common, Phil, Shut up," Frank pretended to scowl, but it became a grin.

"I'm serious." Phil put his beefy, warm hand on my shoulder. "Frank has more than just smarts. He has wisdom. Listen to him, and follow his guidance. And when you go back to school in the fall, be open and receptive to all they can teach you, too."

I nodded again, sipped some beer, thought it through. My mother had said the same thing a thousand times, however, it was different coming from Frank and now Phil.

"What do you do in the winter?" Maggie asked Phil.

"I have a club like this in Boston," he said. "Frank comes in once and a while and helps me abuse a few of my customers."

"He's also a good businessman and entrepreneur. What he really loves is poetry and writing songs," Frank added.

"If you like, I'll sing a song about you at the 11:00 show," Phil said.

"Have you thought it up already?" Maggie asked, tilting her head toward him.

"Let's work on it right now. What's your favorite color?"

"Chartreuse."

Frank and Phil were off –

"No use!"

"Let loose!"

"Fat goose!"

"Big Moose!"

"Love juice!"

"Self abuse!"

The louder they got, the more attentive the rest of the patrons became, and pretty soon they had everyone's attention.

"Tooth loose!"

"Foot loose!"

"Gay muse!"

As if in a duel, both of them speeded up. They were going so fast no one else thought of jumping in.

"Belarus!"

"Hangman's noose!"

"Vamoose!"

"Obtuse!"

"For sooth!"

"Dr. Seuss!"

By now they were laughing too hard to continue, and the match was declared a tie. They shook and Frank ordered another round. Leaning toward me he said, "Study what's going on here, it's your sociological lesson for today. If you want to lead a really rich life, observe everything, every single thing! Open your eyes and your mind and see what's really taking place."

"You won't see this in Plymouth," Phil laughed and gestured at the full room. "Whites and blacks, rich and poor, highly educated and drop outs, gays and straights, big city folks and country bumpkins–all having a good time together. My place is the polar opposite of bars advertising a fight every Saturday night."

He was right. The crowd was loud, raucous, with intense sexual energies radiating thru the room like a bursting sun; and yet, the thought of serious disagreement seemed remote.

"Oh, look," Phil tapped my shoulder and pointed to the stage. "Pay attention."

An ancient woman sat down at the piano. Four inches of fading red hair spiraled up on top of her head contrasting with her bright pink summer dress. "Blue Tango" by Leroy Anderson pulsed through the room. Even my untutored ear recognized a pro.

"She used to give voice lessons in New York," Phil said, "But both her sons died in the war, her husband committed suicide and she hasn't sung since. Mozart and Puccini are her favorites but it doesn't go over as well here as in the city. She helps me manage the club in Boston, and this fall I may send her to Key West to open another place down there."

"Can you get Natasha and me a job on Broadway?" asked Maggie.

"Maybe off Broadway, Hartford or Boston, but I wouldn't be

doing you any favors. They don't pay enough to buy pet food, never mind the rent."

"Still though," she pouted. "That's what we really, really want."

"There's a lot of new stuff going on, they call it the theater of the absurd. Usually it's about helpless people leading meaningless lives. They're so bored with their own existence they end up jumping off tall buildings."

"Sounds dramatic," Maggie smiled. She moved her feet, and that's when I noticed she wasn't wearing shoes.

"About as dramatic as you can get," Phil agreed.

I started on my second beer. No matter how hard I tried, I couldn't stop stealing glances at her naked feet. She'd kicked off her light summer sandals and her toes with their magnetic red nails, looked delicious. She had round heels, lovely, well-rounded, heels. *Am I drunk?* Her bare feet led to images of her beautiful body. She could just slip out of her dress and she'd be completely naked (except for the choker) ready to hop into bed. The more I tried to stop thinking, the more vivid my thoughts became.

Frank kept two cigarettes going in his own private ashtray and another in his hand. Natasha was equally intense about smoking–big gulps in through her mouth and exhaled from her nose. I tried smoking a couple of Luckys in a row to make me look older but the smoke started to irritate my eyes. After the fourth round of beers, I fell behind. I didn't like the taste, knew I was in over my head and had run out of things to say. I noticed that neither of the girls was sitting next to me. Maybe I had gone a little heavy on the aftershave, or maybe it was my adolescent pimples. I caught Frank's eye and glanced at the door. Frank smiled with understanding.

"Skip, Old Dog, I hate to cut your evening short, but do you mind taking care of that business on the boat that we talked about?"

Business? Oh. Right. I nodded. "Sure, I'll handle it."

"What business?" Eddie asked.

"Such a leetle boy and you make heem vork so hard," Natasha said.

"I'll take care of it," I said. "Nice meeting everyone."

A chorus of *Nice to meet you! Hope to see you again!* And from Eddie, *You sure you won't get lost?*

It took about 20 minutes to walk back to the wharf. I was sorry to miss out on Phil's chartreuse song, but I knew Frank would re-enact it for me verbatim in the morning. In my bunk, I read for a while, but fell asleep before the rest of the crew came in.

The next morning there was a general rehashing of the evening's events. Didn't sound like I missed much, and most of what they told me had taken place before I left. I was struck by Frank's recall of detail–he was able to quote exact chunks of dialogue–and wondered if he had a photographic memory.

Over the next few days the stories grew, developed and took on the teller's personality with each reiteration. From the way Eddie spoke, you'd think he'd spent the night with Maggie and Natasha both! As is often the case, the stories became better than the reality.

As time passed, some of the novelty began to wear off and while I still found it exciting to go out with the rest of the crew, I noticed that Troy and Rolly were opting to return earlier and earlier with me. Finally there came a night when even Frank said, "Wait up, Old Dogs, Eddie and I are coming too." Waking up at 3:30 was enough to cramp anyone's social life.

The Laws Of Changeless Justice

Nothing grows faster than a fish from when it bites until it gets away.

Unknown

As I let the dock lines go one morning, I almost tripped over three sleeping figures curled up near the wheelhouse. "Whoa!" I said. "Frank, who are these guys?"

"College kids from New York City. They work at the Atlantic House. Never been on a boat before, so I told them it was okay to bring along a blanket and keep us company. We'll be back in time tonight to get them to work. Just make sure they're out of the way when we're setting out and hauling back our gear–be damn sure nobody gets hurt."

David was from Queens, Barry came from Brooklyn, and they both went to school at the City University of New York. The third guy, Vinny, lay curled up and green despite the flat-ass calm. David and Barry more than made up for his inactivity; they were all over the boat with a never-ending stream of questions, and clearly relished this change in their daily routine.

"Hey, Skip, where are we?" David asked.

"In the middle of Cape Cod Bay, on the east side, or down slope of Stellwagen Bank, just south of a place called the Mussels. Isn't it beautiful?"

"Better than being in P'town all day," Barry replied. "Look at the water, it's clear as gin and when you look deeper it becomes green and then deeper blue."

"There are whales feeding over there, see the spouts?" I pointed off our bow. "And bluefish chasing mackerel, and sharks all around us. Welcome to the big fish tank."

Fleetingly impressed, David and Barry watched in silence for a while, but then their mouths got restless and they started arguing about the conflict in Korea.

"It'll be a flaming disaster," Barry predicted. "It'll lead to a war with Red China and Russia against us. Personally, I don't give a rat's ass about a bunch of hilly rice paddies. Other than the draft, will it make one iota of difference in the way you wake up tomorrow morning which way it goes?"

"Oh sure, leave out the only thing that really matters," David said. "Namely, one little atom bomb and it's all over."

"We'll never use an A-bomb," Frank declared firmly. "Hell's bells, it's not even a 'war', it's just a horseshit 'conflict'. I'd bet the money of this entire trip we never win this stupid thing."

"I don't think Dave or I can cover that bet Frank, but I'll wager a martini in Manhattan you're wrong," Barry said.

"What do you think of Korea, Skip?"

"Well, I don't pay much attention to that kind of stuff."

"I'll tell you this, Joseph McCarthy, that paranoid pecker checker, is going to blacklist all of us," Frank said. "He's after pinko professors, schools, everybody. Probably wants to fry my ass because I read *War and Peace* and know the difference between Lenin and Trotsky."

"I've got a professor, born in St. Petersburg, talks about Marx and Engels and the *Manifesto* every day. Rumor is he'll be gone next semester," Barry said.

"That's when it gets you, when it happens here. People judging you for your beliefs."

"Like your religion or your race."

On and on they went. I heard names I recognized - Alger Hiss, the Rosenbergs, and Governor Dewey - but couldn't identify, and tried to keep out of it. "You think the ends justify the means, Skip?"

"Uh, sometimes."

"He's right," Frank said. "Sometimes they do. But sometimes they don't. Now you take a guy like Senator McCarthy..."

Of course what bothered me wasn't their conversation but my own ignorance. Growing up in Plymouth made me a Provincial Pilgrim in the way so typical of little towns and small thinking. The contrast between these city boys and me was shocking and shameful.

"Ever been to Manhattan, Skip?" David asked.

"Couple of times. I got a friend who drives an eighteen-wheeler. Sometimes he invites me to keep him company when he goes down to Fulton Fish Market on the lower East Side."

"We've got some great baseball if you ever want to catch a game. Have you gone to the Empire State Building or Birdland?"

"No, just the fish auction." They exchanged glances and I felt defensive, compelled to make my visits sound exciting and evocative.

"Fishermen in New England sell to local buyers like Reliable Fish Company in Plymouth, and they ship to larger buyers in New York. One of Reliable's major buyers is a guy named Hymie Buyer." I waited for them to laugh and they did. "I thought it was a fake name he made up, but that's his real name. Anyway, at 5:00 every morning, Sunday through Thursday, there's an auction at the Fulton Fish market. The auction price varies, depending on the amount of fish landed, the species, freshness and other variables, but fundamentally, it follows the law of supply and demand and ultimately determines the amount of money each individual in the supply channel receives."

They nodded, more to be polite than impressed with knowledge.

After lunch, Frank climbed into the lifeboat and recited *"Gloire De Dijon*" and *"Transmitters"* by D. H. Lawrence. Then in full voice he raced on to Robert Herrick's *"Upon The Nipples of Julia's Breast":*

Have ye beheld (with much delight)
A red rose peeping through a white?
Or else a cherry (double grac'd)
Within a lily? Center placed?
Or ever mark'd the pretty beam,
A strawberry shows, half drown'd in cream?

Eddie cut off two codfish heads and stuck them under his shirt. "Varoom, Varoom!"

"Nice jugs!" Rolly picked up a small haddock and threw it at Eddie. "Mama Mia, what bazongas!"

"Great lungs!"

David and Barry began chanting, "Take it off, take it all off!"

"Such a pair!"

"Put those big, soft, lovely, roses where my nose is!"

Eddie removed them from his chest and threw one at Frank. "You sure you don't think it smells like fish?"

While the wire cable snapped onto the winch, Barry climbed into our dory/ lifeboat and stood in the bow imitating Frank. In a clear, confident voice he paraphrased Captain Bligh:

Cast me adrift in your orange dory will you?
Three thousand miles from the nearest port of call.
I'll see you all (for enhanced drama, he pointed to each of us)

hanged from the highest yardarm in Provincetown Harbor, Sirs!

Frank saw this as the highest possible form of compliment and shouted back:

The laws of changeless justice bind
Oppressor and oppressed;
And close as sin and suffering joined,
We march to fate abreast.

The only one not enjoying the performance was Vinny, who took that opportunity to crawl to the side and throw up.

"Thank you," laughed Frank, "You're a beautiful audience!"

We emptied the bag; reset the net and then the deck deteriorated into a no-holds barred fish fight. Everything from whole fish to gobs of guts flew everywhere. Finally Frank reluctantly called a halt because the windows in the pilothouse were so dense with fish guts and gurry that he couldn't see.

The net came back in again and now telltale black, triangular fins swirled around the bag as we hauled it closer to the side. Small fish escaping out the wings of the net attracted three large Blue Sharks. Eddie ran into the pilothouse to get my .22 rifle, came back up and cranked off a couple of quick shots.

"What's the biggest shark you've ever seen?" David asked.

"A twelve-hundred pound White," Eddie said. "When I was on the gill netter *Geraldine and Phyllis*. February, 1938, one of the coldest days of the winter, we were four miles east of the Gurnet and this crazy damn shark got all tangled up in our gear. God, what a mess! Took us hours to get it even half straightened out. Shark never should have been in there, especially at that time of year. We threw the gill net away, nothing left but tangled twine. We didn't have any way to heist the shark on board so we towed it all the way back to the dock. Sold it to a buyer in Boston for twelve dollars, a penny for each lousy pound. Probably ground it up for cat food."

The sharks swimming around the Stanley weren't dangerous, but at two hundred pounds with large, sharp teeth, they could have torn a hole in the net and caused us to lose fish from the last set. Nor was the little .22 a real threat unless you hit a shark dead on at very close range.

The altercation provided only brief respite, and chatting resumed when Barry pointed at Vinny and said, "You can't tell, but he's going to play in the pros. He's already in the semi-pros, guaranteed he'll make it all the way to the top."

"You're going to need him, 'cause the Red Sox are on fire!" Frank shouted. "With Pesky and Ted Williams, you damn Yankees'll be begging for mercy come October."

"What, you never heard of Whitey Ford? You must have your head under a fish barrel because Joe Di Maggio will make that tiny little ball park of yours look like a sandlot in Queens when he starts hitting," David said.

"His kid brother, Dom's the one to watch, Joe's an old fart, ready to retire. He can't even pick his nose, never mind a fast ball coming in over his letters," Rolly added.

To my relief, we were back at MacMillan Wharf. I eased the *Stanley* into the slip, and with Vinny in the lead, our visitors started to leave.

"Come into the A House tomorrow night and we'll buy. Maybe we can do a poetry jam. I don't think they're ready for a swearing gig, but who knows," Barry said.

"Why don't you guys come down to the city this fall," David added, "We'll show you our town– take in a game, go to a show, do some touristy stuff."

I didn't know if they were sincere about wanting to see us again or if the offer was obligatory, but Frank's gracious reply, that we'd be sure to look them up next time we were in town, was perfect. Vinny, finally upright and waiting impatiently on the dock, said, "Thanks! Bye!" The rest of us shook hands and watched them leave.

"Listening to them talk, I feel like the world's biggest idiot," I admitted to Frank.

"What? Why?"

"They knew so much about the world. All I know is fish."

I was surprised when he laughed. "Well," he said, "those city boys thought you were a genius."

"Yeah, right."

"I'm serious. Barry didn't believe it when I told them you didn't want to finish High School. He said *Bullshit!* But I told him I've got all summer and 500,000 pounds of codfish to convince you!"

"Why, though? I didn't say a single word, just sort of agreed with everything they said."

"Exactly," he nodded. "That's a real talent, Skip. Lotsa guys, like me, have to put our two-cent's worth in about everything. But I say if you really want to impress someone, you keep quiet. Nod a lot. And people think you're Einstein."

"Funny!" I replied. But like everything he said, it made perfect sense.

We left early the following morning, worked the next day on the backside of the Cape, and started home to Plymouth late that night with the fish hold full.

Lightning flashed in the west. While still too far away to hear the thunder, we were headed directly towards each other; there was no question about it. I said a small prayer of thanks for the stunning fireworks display I was about to witness. The anticipation felt like caffeine. Thunderstorms always fascinated me, but out here on the open ocean with no hills, buildings, or trees to interfere with the view, the undisputed and unrivaled power of storms was incredible.

In the pre-dawn light I could see distant curtains of darker, gray-green rain approaching. The storm looked a little north of west traveling easterly at about 20 miles per hour while we steamed west at nine knots. I changed course left by 25 degrees, noted the time and new course, shut off the depth finder and radio, and checked all the hatches. The lazarette and engine room were all buttoned up, the doors were inside the rail and secure, the net lay folded on the deck, the Gilson block was tied off and I went to half speed. That would bring Frank up on deck to see what was going on. He had his own bunk in the small wheelhouse, but he rarely used it because it overflowed with charts, mending twine, fuses, cans of engine oil, clothes and assorted other debris. Usually he slept in the fo'castle, occupying the bunk vacated by whoever was at the wheel.

Time is such a slippery thing. Tired and bored, the first half hour of this watch seemed endless. The radio was often my only companion this early in the morning, and no one minded me playing it at full volume: Muddy Waters, The Ames Brothers, Tony Bennett, Louie Armstrong. I sang "Blueberry Hill" at the top of my lungs, and paced the two or three steps in front of the wheel to keep myself alert. My off-key renditions of "If I Knew You Were Comin' I'd've Baked a Cake" and "Ragg Mopp" were atrocious. Soon I changed the station to hear "Buttons and Bows." Dreamy, sleepy music out of Boston, the antidote for all the insomniacs– "My Heart Cries for You," "Sentimental Me," and "Silver Bells" were not what I needed, but my favorites, "Night Train with Woo Woo Ginsberg," or "Jumping with Symphony Sid" were off the air. WWVA, the country and western station out of Wheeling, West Virginia was a short, ineffectual diversion.

But now, with the approaching storm, time rushed by much too quickly. I scanned the horizon, left to right, right to left. No one here but us chickens! Unless a boat appeared from the other side of this storm headed towards us, there was no need to worry about a collision. Slipping the two little ropes over the spokes of the wheel, I stepped out on deck, closed the doghouse doors and felt the first cold drops of rain penetrate my thin T-shirt. I stood on the hatch covers and watched in awe as lightning struck the sea. The thin, white electric discharge hit our liquid world and everything seemed connected. The electricity, the water and the air seemed to fuse, to become one. Could this be what Einstein's equations attempted to explain? Should've paid more attention in science class!

Frank ran across the deck and opened the wheelhouse door. Sure enough, my change of speed had woken him. He looked around, his expression alert, and touched my shoulder. "We'll sure as hell need the umbrellas, Old Dog. How long do you think it'll be 'til we hit the edge of this squall?"

I shrugged, suddenly gloomy. I knew what was coming.

He pointed. "We're doing eight or nine miles an hour, and the storm is traveling about twice that. We're roughly two miles away. So that means less than 5 minutes. See?"

I thought *No* but answered, "Yes." We both lit cigarettes and I thought about how successful I'd been at avoiding this kind of calculation in class.

The storm swooped in suddenly, sheets of rain blowing at a thirty-degree angle with powerful beauty. A hissing sound, then BOOM. Temporarily blinded by the light and deafened by the noise I shouted, "Is everything okay? Did I forget anything?"

Frank took it all in at a glance before he entered the wheelhouse, but to honor my questions he took another careful look. "Finest kind, Capt., finest kind."

We passed through the hail, through the wind shifts, through the rain again, and quickly came out into a clear, rain-washed morning shimmering in the silvery sun. A glowing rainbow lit up our lee side, brighter than normal against the gray, green storm clouds.

Frank opened the wheelhouse windows, took a deep breath. "God, it's a great time to be at sea!"

I agreed. There was simply no other feeling that could compare to invigorating open air.

"I've been watching you and I know you enjoy working," Frank said.

I nodded.

"How's your math?"

"Enh."

"You could have figured out how long it would take to meet the squall line–it's really simple. Try to look at it like it's a game, something that's fun to do. The reward is knowing something you didn't know before."

"It's hard for me," I said. I didn't add *Especially when I've been awake for twenty hours!* because I knew he was trying to help me.

"Most people avoid the hardest of all work–sustained and continuous thinking. It looks easy. You see someone sitting, relaxed–no movement, no sweat. But just try it for one hour. Think about one subject; one only, and examine every facet of your thought. See how you feel at the end of one full hour."

"Is that why I hate school so much? Because it takes thinking?"

"I don't believe so. It's more your inability to see a practical use for the instruction. Remember, that little girl with glasses and mosquito bites on her chest may work a hell of a lot harder than you do. That's why she aces all those tests. You might just ask her for some help with algebra; she could also be a lot hornier than you think."

"Really?"

"You never know until you ask. If you find it hard working at home, go to the library. Working with your brain is much more important than working with your back. Ask Edison or Einstein, even Eddie."

"Okay, I'll call Edison and Einstein when we get to town," I said.

He smiled, but rubbed his temples. That meant he had one of his headaches. "Go grab some sleep before we unload," he said.

"Okay."

I rolled into my bunk, grateful to be warm and dry and allowed to sleep. But I tried to take his advice and concentrate on one thought: How can we live in a world where water fills the air, and yet we don't drown?

Think, think... but within a few minutes, sleep took over.

With fish prices high, we unloaded in Plymouth at the Town Pier. Frank stayed behind to collect our payment while Eddie moved the boat over to the State Pier to take on more ice. It felt strange to finish in the middle of the day, but we had worked for 36 hours with just a few scattered naps. We cleaned the fish hold, washed down the deck, hung the net to dry, greased the engine and changed the oil by the time Frank returned.

"Come on, come on! Everybody in the fo'castle. Asses and elbows below, we're going to settle up!"

We followed him down and he slapped a thick wad of money on the table. "We're rich, we're rich!" He pulled money out of every pocket. "Sonova bitch, we're rich!"

"My God, Capt., did you stop and rob a bank?" Eddie asked.

"Not yet!" He laughed. "No, this money is courtesy of Mighty King Neptune. The price of fish shot way the hell up in New York this morning and no one knows why. We hit the market at just the right time. Nobody at Reliable can remember the price being this high in the summer, but screw it, we have the money, let's get out of here and enjoy it!"

"Frank, we're two blocked with ice and fuel, all we need is a little food and we can go right back out," Eddie said, "catch some more money."

"Nah, let's take a break. We'll leave first thing in the morning," Frank said. He put our money in a pile and redistributed it according to the share system. In the early 50's the minimum wage was 75 cents an hour, while the salary for a working man ashore averaged between seventy or eighty dollars a week. I left the fo'castle that afternoon with 93 dollars in my pocket. No one ever mentioned the hours.

As we tied up to the dock, I spotted Paulie the Panty Peeker in his favorite spot under the wharf pretending to be fishing for smelt. He had two small rods, bait and a bottle of extra-cheap muscatel cleverly concealed in a brown paper bag. He looked like an old seagull, thin neck extended, head up, rigid with anticipation. He'd made a career of peeking through the cracks of the pier, hoping some female tourist might unwittingly allow him a brief glimpse of her underwear. On rare occasions an irate Pilgrim Mother or member of the Daughters of the American Revolution would stomp down with a bucket of soapy water from the nearby public toilets and dump it on him from above, but he would rather stay there, soaking wet, than move.

Frank and I were the last to leave that afternoon. Walking down the pier, I said, "Frank, check out this guy." I pointed to a small man, unremarkable until he turned, and Frank stared at the size of his belly.

"Holy shit," said Frank, "He looks like he's ten months pregnant!"

"His name is Junior Kulldemaris. He spends most of his time fishing for tommy cod, flounders, mackerel, or smelt, depending on the season."

"Of all the places for him to be! He looks like he could topple over into the water at any moment! And who among us would be able to save him? We'd need a friggin crane! How come all those people are standing around him? What's going on?"

"He likes to show off and make a little beer money. He bets tourists a dollar that he can skin a live eel without using a knife."

As we walked closer, we saw a two-foot eel wrapped around Junior's forearm, creating a thick coating of white slime on his deeply tanned skin. The tourists, visitors at a freak show, listened as he extolled the life cycle of Anguilla rostrata:

"These amazing creatures are born in deep water southwest of Bermuda in the Sargasso Sea and the transparent young make their way up to the same fresh water streams and rivers their parents came from. Remarkable how they do this when some nights I have trouble finding my way home from the Blue Bird Café. Ha ha ha!"

I uttered a soft, "Amen."

"But little baby eels are pretty good at this celestial navigation stuff or whatever the hell it is they do," Junior went on. "Females spend a couple of years up stream in fresh water and then meet the males again in the brackish estuaries." The stub of a damp home-rolled cigarette hung from the corner of his mouth. "The adults swim all the way back to their traditional breeding grounds, half way to the Azores, release up to four million eggs each, and die. Seems like a rotten life, what with every fish and sea bird known to man thinking that you and all your kinfolk are just about the best thing in the world to eat."

I leaned close to Frank and said, "The first time I heard him I thought he made up a good fish story to go with the rest of his act, but he's got the basic facts right. The Sargasso Sea is one of the saltiest places in the North Atlantic and they go down to the bottom, 250 fathoms, to lay their eggs."

"That's a little deep for us," Frank said. "Besides we'd have to scrub for a week to get rid of all that greasy slime."

Junior's audience grew and I noticed one woman give an obvious tug at her husband's shirt–*This is disgusting, let's go!* but it had the opposite effect and he edged closer to the front.

"Eel is one of my favorite foods," Junior announced grandly. "Normally, I skin them with a knife. But my father was half-Indian and he showed me how to remove their skin without any tools. No knife. No pliers. No nothin'."

One woman said, "Oh!" and took a step back.

"Anyone care to make a friendly wager?" The eel on Junior's arm squirmed and slithered, unaware of its role in the performance.

"How long will it take?" Frank obliged.

"Less than a minute."

"I'll give you a dollar."

"Thank you, Captain."

That Junior addressed him as "Captain" meant nothing to the tourists, but the respectful title on the waterfront was no different from saying, "Good Morning, Judge" in the courtroom. The fact that Frank bought large amounts of food, fuel and ice from local merchants and that several men depended on him to earn money for their bills was understood by the locals.

Junior stunned the eel by slamming its head on the solid wooden planks. Then he bit it just below the head. Inserting his long sharp thumb nail, he peeled down an inch of skin. Junior gave one sure pull, fully extended his arms, and triumphantly displayed an empty skin in one hand and a naked, twitching eel in the other.

"Uuuuhg!" went the crowd. Frank tossed the dollar bill he had been holding into Junior's waiting cap. I threw in some loose change. The tourists took the hint and dug into their pockets. One reported that it had taken 43 seconds. Several stifled gags.

"You can be expert at anything you choose," Frank said as we walked away. "Just be damn sure it's something more than naked eels."

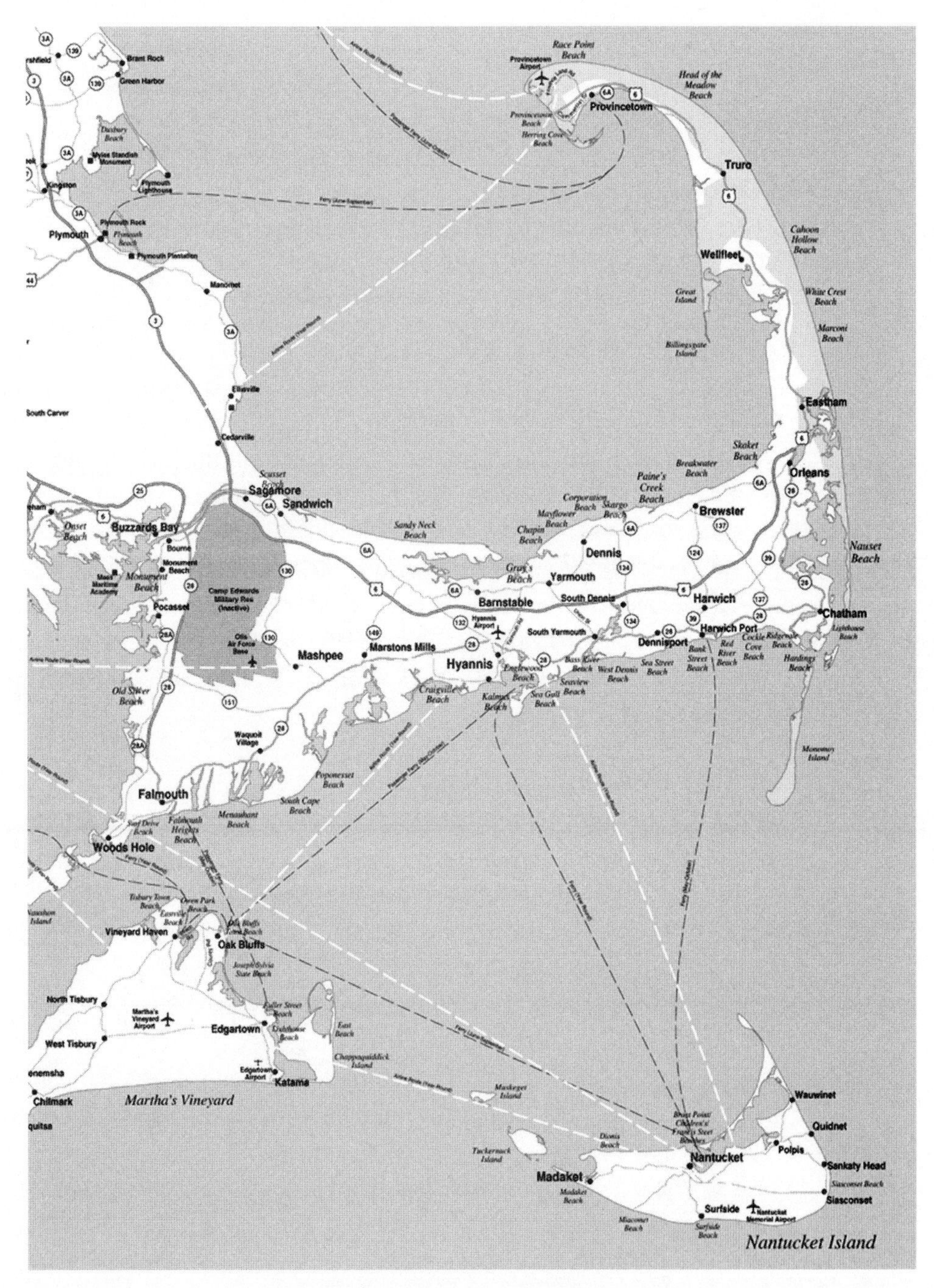

Plymouth, Cape Cod, and the Islands

Lady Luck

Eye-flattering fortune, look thou never so fair,
Nor never so pleasantly begin to smile,
As though thou would my ruin all repair ----

More's Fortune Poems of 1535 – Modernized, Lewis The Lost Lover

We left Plymouth at 1:00 a.m. and set the net on the backside of the Cape by 6:30. At 8:00 we knew we were going to have a great trip. The first tow required two splits to bring all the fish on board. None of us had seen anything like this! Everyone had seen whiting fill the net, but today large yellow tail flounder squirmed in the twine. No need to chop heads here. Just wash, sort by size and ice them down. Even the sorting was easier than usual; 75 percent were large to extra large.

Eddie ran into the wheelhouse. "Finest kind Capt., finest kind!" Picking up Frank, he carried him out on deck and dropped him into the overflowing fish pen as the rest of us cheered. When Frank regained his footing, I raised his right arm.

"The Winner and still Champion of the World!"

"Champion Flounder Finder!" Rolly added gleefully.

"And no one else in sight!" I gestured at the wide-open sea. "Should we throw out a buoy?"

Frank shook his head. "Not while its still daylight. Why let everyone and his brother know about this spot? Let's wait until about eight and then mark just the north side."

The fish kept coming and we worked all day, with short breaks for sandwiches. When I commented on Frank's methodical records about our catches, he said, "I learned from Peter Jorgensen when we fished together on the *Medric.* I can't overstate to you the importance of keeping accurate accounts, Skip."

I nodded. Peter Jorgensen was known to all, a local legend. He fished one area northeast of the Gurnet so consistently that it became known as Pete's Tow, and it was said he knew that area better than his own back yard.

"Skip, be sure to record everything–dates, locations, depths, ranges if you're in sight of land, tides, times, air temperatures, moon phases, length of tows, estimated catches by species and anything else important. You think you'll remember all the details, but you won't. Someday it'll make the difference between being a good fisherman and being one of the best."

"Only reason we're here is because Frank found this spot last year," Rolly said. "Holy Shit, whatta great haul!"

"Think about it, Skip," Eddie's tone was earnest. "Whole wide ocean. One spot that's full of fish. And we come back to the exact same spot?" He glanced with reverence at Frank. "That's talent."

Frank dismissed the compliment modestly. "Usually talent is nothing more than taking the time to do something right."

Whatever it was, Frank's method really paid off. Just before dark we placed a bamboo buoy with a flag at the top, a cast iron window sash weight at the bottom and an old life jacket in the middle. The seas started to increase with the tide running hard.

While we towed away from the marker, Frank called his friend Whitey, owner of the *Gannett*, and told him where we were through a prearranged code. Most skippers had one or two close friends who would share good fishing locations. The challenge was to convey the tip to one individual without alerting the entire fleet. The flip side of the system was that sometimes just the opposite was true, as was the case with Francis "Khaki" Captiva, captain of the *Philasca*, a dragger out of Provincetown. After a terrible day fishing off the Highlands, Khaki decided to share his misery and called half a dozen boats. "Come this way, the fishing is great!" Everyone he spoke to, plus a few more, raced to the backside of the Cape. Seeing Khaki headed back to Provincetown, they assumed he would unload a record catch. The saying "Come this way" became a catch phrase for information that could lead to triumph or disaster.

Eddie became a master at deciphering the subtleties. "Come this way" from one of the Boston boats like the *J. B. Junior II*, usually meant *There's nothing here, I'm leaving*. On the other hand, "Come this way" from a Provincetown boat required positive identification of the speaker, and then clarification of the actual language. "Come on by" could mean no fish. "Come this way, Cap't." might mean fish were plentiful.

"If only we could speak Italian or Portuguese," I said.

"Wouldn't matter," Eddie told me. "Half the fleet knows one or both languages."

"Quit wasting your time," Frank advised. "It's like figuring out the

German U Boat code. Nice to know, but guess what? The war is over."

Eddie and I looked at him, too intrigued to leave it alone.

"Does it matter if they use the word 'fish' in the message?"

"Sure it matters!"

"Really?"

"'Course! Sometimes it means fish, sometimes it means no fish."

Frank spotted an inroad. "Skip, maybe learning another language *would* help you figure this out."

"Nice try," I said, "but no thanks."

"Why not? This is the perfect opportunity! I'm not saying you have to become fluent and learn how to conjugate verbs. But so many of your friends speak Italian or Portuguese. All you have to do is ask them to teach you just a few words. Some day it'll come in handy."

"Problem is, my friends aren't really proud of their heritage, especially the Italians, what with the war and all. They're embarrassed because they don't speak English very well. They always apologize for it."

"Horseshit," Frank muttered and turned away.

By 10:00 pm the *Stanley's* hold was nearly full of fish, with our ice running low.

"We'll fish until midnight," Frank said. "Put all you can in the fish hold and we'll keep our last tow on deck. We should be in Plymouth around 6:00, so all the fish will be on the dock by 7:00 at the latest. That should be fine."

"The weather is going to pick up tonight so we may be a little slower than usual," Eddie said, scanning the skies. "Plus we're riding a little low already. You think we ought to put even more on the deck?"

"Definitely! Pitch some up into the dory too, make sure no one can beat our record."

We left our buoy for the *Gannett*, and headed home with the most fish any of us had ever seen. The *Stanley* moved low and slow in the water, but we didn't care. We had a boatload of money and were headed for the bank. A quick mug up and victory cigarettes before we jumped into the racks.

WHUMP! I woke up, startled. *THUMP!* I could feel the boat rise and drop with a shudder, as we labored into an increasing sea, pitching, yawing and rolling. Steep, ferocious waves forced everyone to grab hold to something stable. The *Stanley* was well designed for fishing in the Gulf of Maine, and although she could have been a little higher in the bow, she handled well in nasty weather.

"We're taking a real pounding," Eddie said, and I knew all four of us were awake.

"Go back and get more beauty sleep," Rolly advised.

"What about you?"

He grinned. "You need it more than me."

I drifted back to an uncomfortable sleep but was frequently jostled awake and had to hang on to stay in my bunk. In my fitful sleep, I dreamed of money. Piles of cash! It was all over the front steps of my house, in the yard and it covered the sidewalk. But each time I tried to gather some up, it disappeared. I tried sweeping it into a fish barrel. Eddie was there, and he handed me a fish pick to stab the bills. I bent further forward, until I felt myself sinking in a stomach-churning spiral.

CRASH! Suddenly I was thrown from my bunk, and found myself upside down in the dark, enmeshed in a sickening tangle of arms, legs, mattresses, loose bunk boards, broken glass, bedding, boots, tomatoes, carrots, pots, clothes and pans. Frigid water was already up to my knees.

"Get up on deck! Get the hell out of there!" Frank shouted. His crisp, effective tone left no room for panic or hesitation.

We groped and fumbled our way up the narrow ladder. Our boots and shoes were sloshing around, lost below in the awful darkness. The *Stanley* moved with a deep, leaden roll, constant spray reaching half way up the mast, drenching us. The seas were agitated, confused, with no clear direction. The wind out of the northeast increased to 35 miles per hour, with gusts to 40; close to gale conditions. A strong moon tide ran at its maximum.

"Son of a bitch! It's gone!" I head Rolly shout. "We lost our whole fucking deck load!"

"What?" It couldn't be true! But it was. One rogue wave had crashed over our port quarter, hit the forward pen board and dumped water into the fo'castle before it cleared our deck. Only a few fish remained.

Bracing myself next to Frank, I could hardly hear his voice as he shouted, "Sometimes two or three waves join together, and suddenly you're facing one that's three times the size it should be. We just hit one!"

"Ughh God," Eddie mourned. "All those beautiful fish."

"Wonder how much money we lost?" I asked.

"Thousands," was Rolly's dour estimate.

Frank made a point to look around–at the fishless deck and at each one of us. "Doesn't look like any of us washed overboard," he said, and we realized how lucky we'd been. Loss of fish, disappointing, but not the end of the world.

Eddie sprang into action. "Come on, Skip," he said, "gimme a hand here!"

I joined him at the hand bilge pump. Facing each other, his right hand at the top, left hand two feet down, and my smaller hands just under his, we worked it, displacing even more water than we could have with the mechanical pump.

"Know that whaling ship the *Pocahontas*? Out of Vineyard Haven?" I asked. Eddie nodded. "Got attacked by a whale. The captain said it took 250 strokes an hour to stay ahead of the incoming water. Think we can do it?"

"I can," Eddie said, "but I'm not a candy ass."

I gritted my teeth to keep up with his swift, powerful strokes.

Rolly slipped and slid towards the engine room. Halfway there he gave a yelp as a splinter from the deck entered his bare foot, but he never slowed down. Frank kept our bow to the wind, with the throttle at a quarter speed, two or three knots, about walking speed.

"Can you handle this alone?" Eddie asked. I nodded. He walked the rail, looking for more damage. Suddenly, I heard him curse and saw him frantically pull in a piece of rope we used as a spring line.

"Dammit!" he shouted. "One end of it washed over the side!"

"If that went into the propeller cage ... we'd be here for a while," Frank said. "More good luck for us!"

Eddie knew that one of the fish hold hatches had washed off. He found it by the stern scupper. "The lazarette hatch lifted," he reported, "but not much water in the engine room."

"Our steering cables intact?" Frank asked.

"Seem to be."

"Good."

Gradually control and stability returned. Troy replaced Eddie to help me at the pump. I was drenched in sweat, despite the windblown spray, but my bare feet were freezing.

"Skip, take these." Frank handed his boots to me and I pulled them on as fast as I could.

Even without our deck load, the ride across Cape Cod Bay took longer than usual. Rolly had turned the lights on in the fo'castle, and I never saw such a mess. Stuff strewn all over the floorboards, soaked from the water.

"These mattresses will never dry. The salt water will make them scratchy forever," Eddie said.

"They picked up some bilge water from the fish hold, and they'll smell like old fish and diesel oil the rest of their lives," Rolly agreed.

"Overboard they go!" said Frank, as we joined in the discard frenzy. Everything went into the hungry sea except some new oilskins and our soggy boots. Rolly put the bunk planks back in place and I scrubbed the entire fo'castle with strong soap and fresh water. After we finished the first cleaning we went back and scrubbed the table, seats and floor again.

Frank stood, stretched his back, then shaded his eyes with one hand. I saw the number one buoy and Gurnet Point, at the tip of Duxbury Beach, loom into view as I moved to stand next to him.

"The Gurnet is a mythical place Skip. Do you think Eric the Red's son is buried here?"

"I hope so, 'cause I told a lot of people on the *Louise* that he is."

"I guess it doesn't matter if it's true or not. It's so much a part of our legacy." Frank took a deep breath, held it, then let it out slowly and with pleasure, something all sailors do. Nothing is more intoxicating than clean salty air. For Frank, it sometimes eased the pain in his head. "Ever wonder what it was like, fishing from a Viking long boat?" he asked. "High in the bow and low amidships, seems it would be easy to haul in large fish over the low-lying gunwales. What stories would Eric the Red have told about his largest codfish? The Norse sailors fished for cod in the same waters we fish–did they use jigs made of bone? What did they use for bait? How did they make their line? Cod were so easy to catch and so available, with only slight seasonal adjustments, that no one would ignore this readily available source of protein."

"Do you think the Norse raiders entered the inner harbor and camped near our homes?"

"I don't know. Scholars disagree on whether the Vikings actually came as far south as Plymouth. Some claim to see indisputable evidence of Vikings in Narragansett Bay and along the Rhode Island coast. Others think they didn't sail south of Maine."

"Right." I liked the way he said he didn't know. That was the trouble with my teachers. They'd never admit not knowing something.

They'd just say *Go look it up for yourself!* "Years ago my uncle Deck was stationed at the Gurnet. Back then lighthouses were managed by the United States Lighthouse Service."

"Before it became part of the Coast Guard," Frank said.

"Right. No outboard motors then, so he rowed with the tide to his mother's house on Winslow Street."

"Not much has changed since 1924 when they took down the Northeast Light, half of the pair of twin lights that stood there," Frank commented. "Still, it's a good landmark to guide fishermen, using basic triangulation, to locate fishing sites."

"Position the little black door of the shed directly under the Gurnet Light, then place the Cordage Chimney and the Bug Light and you would be in my favorite honey hole," I said. "Caught a ton of fish there on the *Louise*."

"In 1566, Queen Elizabeth proclaimed it a criminal act to remove or alter sea marks. The white barn on the point, or the large stand of cedar were essential guides to the approach of harbors long before modern channel buoys. I can't imagine going into Boston without buoys," Frank said.

As the *Stanley* pushed through the heavy seas, Gurnet Point looked especially attractive to me. *Welcome Home*! it seemed to say.

Frank had called Reliable Fish the night before to let them know we were coming in with a huge haul, and they were waiting at the dock for us. In silence, they took in our bedraggled appearance: bruises, bandages, a nasty looking gash on my wrist and Eddie sported a black eye. Probably thought we'd had a knockdown, drag out fistfight! But no one questioned the loss of our deck load as Rolly limped to open the fish hold. The rest of the fleet had taken the day off because of the gale-force winds. We weren't pretty, but we were the only ones with fish.

As we started to unload, the usual crowd gathered; regulars who asked for a fish. "For my cat," was the usual explanation. The woman who always wore a filthy raincoat, overshoes and a babushka. Tilt, who had a tumor on his neck the size of a small cantaloupe. And Buggsy, a young man with enormous buckteeth.

Eddie nudged me. "Too bad his brains aren't as large as his teeth."

Another regular was a frail old lady who weighed about 85 pounds and always dressed in black. Although she spoke little English, she was always respectful. She never asked for fish, just waited at the edge of the dock. I liked the way she stood so patiently, the way she held her head up with such grace, such silent strength. I thought her eyes might see things beneath the surface, at the level of the soul. She never used the cat excuse. Whenever we passed her a fish, she always said, "God bless you! *Grat see ah.*"

Frank, a fully ordained atheist, would reply, "God bless you, too, Mother. Go with God. *Dee nee en tay.*"

With unspoken agreement, we always gave her a prime fish. Sometimes Eddie or I would fillet one for her. The first time I did it, I was about to throw the frame away when she stopped me motioning to her brown paper bag.

"She'll use the head and bones to make a traditional chowder," Eddie explained, "You know, eyeball soup. What you were going to throw away is two big meals for her. Maybe food for a week."

Free food was also gathered and hoarded from other town sites. At church suppers, several blue-haired ladies even requested the remaining chicken bones–seemed everyone had a cat who hungered for fish! We didn't mind. If someone could use the carcasses, so much the better.

Another regular was Frenchy. Nicknamed by Frank who said he looked like an old French safe that should have been thrown away a long time ago. Frenchy was one of the few people that Frank disliked. Large, soft and lazy, he was as pale as a vampire–the antithesis of Frank's tanned, quick body. He shuffled, toes dragging, head down, his greasy, uncombed black hair falling forward. He appeared to be thirty years old and never worked. Once, when he passed in front of Sampson's Fish Market, I heard old man Sampson yell the ultimate insult, "Draft Dodger!" In our small town most residents cared for people who needed a little extra help–men traumatized by war, several epileptics and a couple of just plain crazies. Frenchy was none of these. He was a freeloader, first class.

Frenchy sauntered up to where Frank and I stood at the sorting table filling fish boxes with the few haddock we landed as by-catch. "Could I have a fish for my cat?"

I had my hand on a medium, three-pound haddock and was about to toss it to him.

"Unh, could I have that one?" Frenchy asked, gesturing at Frank, who was holding an extra large haddock.

According to New England legend, the cod is sacred because Jesus used them in his miracle of feeding the multitudes. The devil, being jealous, tried to duplicate the achievement with a haddock, but the fish escaped. The haddock retains those distinctive black imprints just behind the gills, where Satan's fiery thumb and forefinger left burn marks. Frank held up a truly beautiful haddock that weighed at least eight pounds. Its especially dark lateral line and the large devil's thumbprint appeared a brilliant black against its silvered body.

"You want this fish?" Frank asked.

Frenchy nodded.

Frank turned, stepped away from the sorting table, and let go. We heard the fish hit the water 15 feet below with a loud *SPLASH*.

Frenchy ambled away, slowly nodding his head as if in agreement with himself saying something like "I never should have asked for the biggest fish, ended up with nothing."

"Waddlesome sloth," Frank said. I never understood how a man could live with some combination of not caring or not knowing about his self-respect. Such a dim dick. If I'd given him that fish he'd probably have asked me to fillet it and cook his dinner, do everything except eat it. I'll bet he still asks his poor old mother to burp him."

Even without the fish we lost overboard during the storm, we landed a big trip with the price for yellow tail flounders remaining high.

Frank took off his gloves, lit a fresh cigarette and said, "Skip, finish up here. I'll go talk to the buyers."

"Okay."

Standing at the sorting tray, I thought I had never seen so many, and I was even wondering if it qualified as a record breaking haul when I became aware of Frank's rising voice. I looked up and saw him talking to Salvador Salucchi. Frank's temper was legendary, and Sal wasn't one to back down, and within seconds the negotiations had turned to a shouting match.

"Impossible! Absolutely not!" Frank hollered.

"Look at the God damned numbers, Frank!" Sal hollered back.

Frank, his face and neck red with rage, stormed over to the 18-wheeler that held boxes of fish on ice. "Get 'em off the fucking truck! We're gonna weigh everything again!"

"The hell you are!" Sal pointed at his figures. "The numbers don't lie."

"No, but you do!" Frank reached to slide out a box. "Skip! Eddie!

Help me get these out, we're gonna weigh 'em again."

Sal yanked Frank's hand from the fish box. "Leave it alone. Take your money and get the hell off the dock. If we take the time to weigh them again, we may be stuck here and we'll have to dump your whole stinking load right back into the harbor."

Frank pushed him away. "You think you can cheat me? You think you can cheat *me*?"

Sal picked up the hatchet used to nail the lids on the boxes. He was Frank's height, but about 25 pounds heavier. The two men, toughened by a life of hard labor, were no strangers to confrontation. Suddenly, there was a hatchet in Frank's hand too. Tidal waves of testosterone crashed against the fragile beaches of reason. A crowd of onlookers surrounded Frank and Sal, blocking any escape route.

Frank was back in the ring. I saw the competitor's expression on his face. Sal's eyes reflected the determination to defend his honor at any cost; a shrewd businessman who had been in this position many times.

The crowd started to make noises... *Easy does it... Take it easy!* and *He's trying to cheat you, Frank!* But before hatchets were raised, before blood was spilled, before one single threat was made, people in the audience found themselves pushed aside, and entering the circle was none other than the little old lady in black. She stepped between the two bulls, her silent disapproval as menacing as any foe. Frank and Sal stopped, surprised. Still holding her fish, the little lady in black delivered a stern gesture. *Stop this. Right now.* The crowd gasped.

Eddie reached Frank, put his hand on Frank's shoulder, and pulled him away from the crowd. At the same time, one of Sal's relatives stepped in with him. The crowd said, *Ohh...* disappointed; a dud when they were hoping for fireworks.

Like a father, Eddie steered Frank back to the boat. "Jeeus, Capt., what was that grab ass all about?"

"The son of a bitch was trying to cheat us by 700 pounds. That little piece of shit. Six boxes of fish. That feverish, selfish, little money grubbing clod! It's bad enough Mother Nature robbed us last night, we're getting screwed on the dock too!"

"For all the business we bring him, you'd think he'd give us a break," Eddie said.

Frank took several deep breaths and shook out some of the tension in his hands. He wiped the sweat off his forehead. We were surprised when he let out a snort of laughter. "That little old lady saved my ass!"

"Nah, Frank, you woulda beat him."

"You can never be sure." Frank lowered his voice. "Once I saw Sal chop a guy twice his size into kindling. I just wanted our money."

Once Rolly had told me that Frank was different; that he felt fear, but not the way most people did. "Seems like he can put fear in a separate room and close the door," was how Rolly put it. And if Frank did eventually let the demons out of the closet, I never saw it.

It intrigued me how everyone knew Frank was not afraid. He didn't brag, and he appeared almost shy in talking about himself. It wasn't his walk. His gait was ordinary, he did not strut. He held himself erect, but never swaggered. His reputation helped, but it was a small part of the story. I had many more questions about fear, but decided to ask Frank after things cooled down. I felt certain he knew the answers.

Frank went back over to Sal and said, "Get the fish to New York. I hear there might be a strike, I doubt your guy wants to cross a picket line."

Sal nodded and turned to his driver. "Go on Jerry, get out of here."

As the truck pulled out, Frank suggested he and Sal go to the Bluebird Café. Sal quickly agreed.

The Bluebird was not a clean, well-lit place. There were no little cocktail tables on the sidewalk. No waiters in tuxedos, cummerbunds and black ties. No tables reserved for ladies. *A Fight Every Saturday Night* was their slogan, and they didn't always mean on television.

Sipping a Coke (the bartender refused to serve me liquor, he said he knew my mother) I watched the dynamics as Frank and Sal repaired their relationship, even developed a heightened respect for each other. The fish would be weighed again as Hymie Buyer accepted the truckload in New York and, agreeing to use the New York numbers, Sal and Frank shook hands. Sal ordered a round of beers. More conversation, and Frank ordered boilermakers.

For the next three weeks they treated each other with exaggerated politeness, and eventually their relationship evolved to a heightened admiration for each other. They became extra careful about their numbers, but in time they teased and joked with one another about who got better grades in math.

The Perfect Crime

Bold knaves thrive without one grain of sense,
But good men starve for want of impudence.

John Dryden, *Constantine the Great: Epilogue*

As I repaired the chafing gear, a seemingly endless job, Frank motioned me over. "Skip, what's the fastest speed boat you've ever seen?"

"Peg Tavares', the one he uses to give tourists rides. The Navy might have something faster, like a PT boat, but I've never seen one at full speed. I know Peg pretty well. Want me to ask him? He knows everything there is to know about high-speed boats."

"No! Do not say a word to anyone! Understand?"

"Uh, okay, sure."

"Who's this guy, Peg?"

"I don't know his real first name, he's been called Peg since he was in a car accident and had half his leg amputated. But he's the undisputed expert on fast cars and boats. Sometimes someone'll come by with a new boat and the first thing they want to do is race Peg."

"Has anyone ever beat him?"

"Never."

"Does he use special fuel?"

"I don't know. Why?"

Frank, lost in thought, didn't answer. I went back to work.

"What was that all about?" Eddie whispered.

"Not sure," I answered.

Half an hour later Frank said he wanted to see me again. We walked to the far edge of the deck where no one could hear us.

"Are there any PTs in Boston?" he asked.

"I have no idea. Why? They make lousy fishing boats."

"Are the inflatable boats with outboards faster? You know, black rubber ones the commandos use?"

"I don't think so. I've seen the Coast Guard struggling to start them. The motors don't look very reliable. Too little choke and they don't start. Too much and they flood. Either way, it requires a lot of pulling on the starter rope. My uncle Deck says he can row to the Bug Light using less muscle power than it takes to start one of those smoke pots."

"I see," he said.

While we refueled, filled the fresh water tank and iced up, Frank asked us what we knew about the Cordage Company, the largest manufacturer of rope in the world. Did anyone know how many employees they had? If they got paid on Fridays? What time each shift was paid?

Uneasily, I wondered if he was planning to sell the *Stanley*, buy a fast boat and go work at the Cordage Company. It would be a lot easier than what we were doing but nowhere near the money. Surely Frank knew that. Was he planning to go into semi-retirement? Were the headaches getting that bad?

I felt even more apprehensive when he gathered us together and announced that he wouldn't be going with us on the next trip.

"We'll be a man short?" I asked, trying to hold back my concern.

"Yes, but you four can handle things. Eddie will be the skipper and Rolly the mate. I'll see you when you come in."

No one asked a single question. We just nodded and said *Okay, yeah, sure.*

We left the next morning with a sense of displacement. To dissipate it, we worked harder than usual. We missed Frank, we were curious and nervous about why he was taking time off, but we were happy to support Eddie in his role as leader. His natural good humor and willingness to help on deck made working one man short bearable. As soon as the net was down and the path in front of us clear, he would secure the wheel and start sorting fish.

Two and a half days later, we were on our way back in and Frank greeted us at the dock. He looked great. Tanned, fit and rested. He was also glad to see us. Eddie had talked to him several times on the radio, so Frank already knew we had eight thousand pounds of haddock, fourteen thousand of cod and four thousand yellowtail, plus a few boxes of butterfish, whiting, blue-hake and wolf-fish.

We unloaded, cleaned up and then Frank called us down to the fo'castle. It was strange to see him fresh and clean-shaven when the rest of us were exhausted and smelling of three-day old gurry.

"You guys did a great job! Thanks for covering me. Any problems?"

We exchanged looks, shook our heads. Nope. None.

"Good," he said. "Well, I won't keep you in suspense any longer. I met with some old friends in Providence and I want to talk to you about something that's illegal as hell."

I felt my eyes grow wide. *Illegal?* "What old friends?" I heard myself ask.

"Old business acquaintances, young Skip," Frank grinned. His eyes were merry. I realized he was talking about contacts in the underworld. Mafia types, smalltime hoods.

"Oh." Time to shut up and listen.

He grew stern. "This conversation is about unlawful shit. The kind of stuff you go to jail for. Some of you have families and kids and responsibilities. Walking out of this discussion now will in no way affect your job on this boat. All I ask is that you never mention any aspect of what you've heard so far to anyone. That means *no one*."

Eddie, Rolly, Troy and I just stared. Rolly had lit a match a few seconds ago, got distracted by Frank's announcement, and hissed "Damn!" as it burned his finger. He blew it out and went back to staring. "If anyone wants to leave, now is the time to go."

No one blinked. No one was going anywhere. It was so silent that I could hear Eddie breathing.

"Okay, then. No talking to your wife, your brother, your mother; not another sweet-cheeked individual. We need to be especially careful of talking in bars."

"Jesus, Capt. Get off the pot! Tell us what the hell is going on!" Eddie exploded.

"Okay." Frank glanced at the door and lowered his voice, as if eavesdroppers lurked. "I've been talking with some people to see who might be doing a little smuggling. If we met a freighter coming into Boston or New York, we would pick up a few packages of diamonds or pearls or anything like that and meet our contacts any where on the East Coast."

My mouth dropped open. Smuggling diamonds?

"You okay, Skip?"

I nodded. Sure, smuggling diamonds! Happens all the time! "So what did they say?"

"No one expressed an iota of interest. The only thing they want to talk about is drugs. Heroine, cocaine. They told me that's how to make serious money. Work for two or three years and retire. I have no intention of getting involved with that, but I told them I'd think about it. So I left Providence and went to Brooklyn. Don't forget, New York City is the diamond capital of the country."

With very little effort, I could see him as a rich man; brown and white shoes gleaming in the dim fo'castle, a fine linen shirt impeccably pressed–he could have been seated at a large teak table in the heart of the financial district "But they said the same damn thing. Drugs. I had one guy offer to buy the *Stanley* right there on the spot. Cash. I told him I would discuss it with my associates. It's bad form to tell no directly."

"Could we really work for two or three years and then retire?" Eddie wanted to know.

"In theory, yes, but it isn't that simple. These businessmen don't like to see people leave their organizations. It creates a vacuum that disrupts their distribution channels. The other major problem is where do you put all this money without people asking questions? Fishermen don't just walk into the Plymouth Five Cents Savings with a hundred thousand dollars and not raise an eyebrow or two. It can be done but it gets complicated. The biggest problem is doing several criminal activities like smuggling, tax evasion, illicit substances, dealing with known criminals and all that stuff over a prolonged period of time."

"Still. If it means not working the rest of my life," Eddie said.

I stood, opened a Coke, sipped it and gripped the bottle hoping no one could see my stupid hands shaking. Rolly's cigarette remained unlit, hanging from the corner of his mouth.

Frank sighed. "I just don't want anything to do with the drug business. Drugs screw up a person's life in the worst way. Way worse than alcohol. If we'd all been born thirty years ago, we could have smuggled liquor and made a fortune."

He paused and lit a cigarette. It was true; most of the boat owners I knew remembered prohibition with great affection. Nor had I ever met anyone who suffered from the ban. Most small boat owners viewed rum running, or "bottle fishing"' as a way to supplement their incomes beyond their wildest dreams. Occasionally, the bottles got mixed up. Charlie Rose told me about a time he'd bought a bottle of ginger ale, only to discover when he opened it that it was pure well-aged whiskey.

"I saw a lot of drugs at Alcatraz," Frank went on to dissuade

Eddie, whose eyes had started to glitter with thoughts of riches. "I want nothing to do with that. I'd rather steal a few tax dollars from the government, or bilk large corporations. The bigger the better. I mean, Christ. Those millionaires and their insurance companies wouldn't even feel a pinch if they lost one week's payroll."

"Right. Fat cats," Eddie agreed, accommodating Frank's plan.

"The Cordage Company has the largest payroll in town. Suppose we bought a small speedboat, one of those Navy Seal types that are really fast mothers, and loaded it into our fish hold... go out and work the Northeast Tow. Three of us run in to the Cordage Company, pick up the money and hightail it back to the *Stanley*. Two of us stay out here fishing and talking on the radio so we all have an alibi. We'll fish close to another boat, maybe even be a pain in his ass so he'll remember we were with him all night long." Frank paused, looked at us one at a time. "What do you guys think?"

"Pure genius," Eddie declared. "It's never been done before, a robbery, a major heist, using a getaway boat."

"We can create a diversion to move the guards away from the money," Rolly added. "A small fire at night in the dining hall or the library will draw everyone."

"Everyone'll assumed we're making our getaway in a car. Dozens of road blocks and we're out beyond the Gurnet. Hooowee! It's a beautiful thought!" Eddie laughed.

"I've done something like this," I said. "It was on a much smaller scale, but I rowed to the lumber yard at the foot of Robin's Road. I wrapped the oars in cloth to muffle the noise, got there around ten." They were all listening attentively so I went on, "I hopped over the fence. There were three lines of barbed wire at the top. No problem. I'd planned for them. The oak laths were outside and easy to find. I pitched over three bales and was off. I built my first set of lobster pots from them."

Everybody laughed. I omitted the second part of the story, which featured my conscience as the main character. The damn thing never let up. I couldn't enjoy the lobsters in those pots, so I took the profits from the lobster business and bought three bales of oak slats. I rowed back, threw the slats over the fence into the lumberyard, and called it even. Hardened criminal to the core.

"I'm sure your expertise will come in handy," Frank chuckled.

"But how will we actually get the money?" Troy asked. "Just ask the guards to hand it over? What if it's in a safe?"

"We have some research to do," Frank said. "The success or failure of this will depend on how well we do our homework. We need to gather information, but we need to be careful. We can't try to get it all at once. Eddie, start looking for the fastest boat there is. We'll need room for three people and big bundles of cash. Maybe you could call some people in Gloucester and New Bedford."

"Okay."

"Skip, Rolly... you know anyone who works at Cordage?"

Rolly nodded. "I got a friend works there."

"Tell him you're thinking of getting a job onshore this winter. Tell him to keep it quiet, you don't want me finding out you're looking for other work."

"Tell him you want to be a guard. Then ask if they work at night, if they're armed," I said.

"Good idea." Frank sent me a glance of respect and surprise. "And back off if you think he's getting suspicious. It's better to get too little information than have folks getting curious and nervous about our little project."

"Let's do some fishing in the Cordage channel tomorrow," I said. "They're biting like crazy right in front of the Cordage dock. We can take my dory and I have all the gear we need. It'll be a great dry run."

"A busman's holiday. Hot shit! What time do you want us on board Captain?"

Everyone laughed but I said, "Four-thirty," with a straight face. My boat, my call. Frank's silent nod said "affirmative." He knew a good leader must also be a good follower.

Casing The Joint

Many go fishing all their lives
Without knowing that it is not fish they are after.

Henry David Thoreau

Frank and Eddie were on the dock at 4:20. As I greeted them, I sensed their excitement. Anticipation of our "research" or pleasure at the idea of fishing just for fun? Maybe a little of both. For me, it was all about the money. Retiring before I turned 21 became my top priority.

"Here she is," I said, and waited while they appraised my boat, a sleek 16-foot double bank dory, painted black for night raids.

"Bigger than I thought," Frank said, impressed. "Two can row."

"Yeah. Eddie, if you'll get in the middle seat, I'll take the forward one."

They hesitated; not second-guessing my direction, but unaccustomed to having me in charge. "Frank, you're in the stern, okay?" I added.

"Why don't you sit in the middle?" Eddie asked.

"That would make the dory bow heavy. Dories are awkward to steer with the bow down."

"Gotcha."

"Frank, maybe you can take the fifth oar and be our helmsman."

"Yes sir!" He threw me a snappy salute.

We got in and assumed our positions, Eddie and Frank relaxed and happy as kids, with mischief in the air. Frank, Hollywood handsome, wore his lucky fishing cap. His military length hair was dark with enough gray to make him look serious. His forearms could be the model for Popeye, bulging with muscle and stand up veins, good for rowing.

Eddie knew how to row–dip just the blades in the water and turn your wrists for that extra kick called feathering. He also possessed the powerful legs and back that rowing demands. Halfway to the Cordage channel, I realized I was really going to have to work to keep up with him.

"What did you bring for bait?" Frank asked.

"Live eels. They've been on ice all night."

"Good, they'll be sleepy and easy to handle."

I nodded at the cooler and he opened it to see. "Beautiful!"

"To fishermen and bass," I grinned. Fourteen inches long, fat and juicy, they were dark blue-green fading to yellow with pure white bellies. Real lookers.

Frank pointed at the bucket. "What's in there?"

"Striper worms."

"I can never figure out how something that lives in the gray, dull mud can acquire such gentle radiance. It seems to go against the laws of nature."

"Yeah. Usually I get my own. I've been digging and selling worms since I was ten. But yesterday I walked into Dupree's and paid for them."

"Where do you dig yours?"

"My favorite place is in front of the old clam factory building, across from Edes' Mill. After a good tide the flat looks like a crudely plowed field with the mud tilled by guys like me, looking for worms. I use a 'sissy' clam hoe with eight-inch tines. On good tides of ten feet or more, I'll see commercial diggers out there using monster hoes with seventeen-inch tines. It takes a lot of strength to pull the mud with my small hoe that's half the size of theirs! I see them rubbing their backs and complaining. Once I saw a guy pass out, I think he had a heart attack. The ambulance came and got him."

"Hard work," Eddie said.

"Very. Bend over, bury the tines, pull the mud back and pick out the worms. Bend, bury, pull and pick. But you only do it for four hours–two hours before low tide and two hours after the tide turns. Some commercial diggers dig a double, that is, work a morning tide and an evening tide. One guy I know wears a miner's light on his head so he can extend his digging time.

They nodded. I fell silent, remembering not the labor, but the beauty. On certain days early in the season, the mud glistened with the colors of water, earth and sky. Like a bucket of paint containing all the primary colors, it looked gray at first. Closer inspection revealed the reds, yellows and blues, hidden from the casual observer. Like any great artist, the Master did not over mix, but left traces of the original pigments for our pleasure.

Frank took a deep breath and let it out. "Here we are, just like the ancient Greeks, rowing out to meet mighty Poseidon, the brother of Zeus. Men rowed wooden boats for thousands of years before Christ, and He had a special place in His heart for all fishermen. He had two sets of brothers as disciples, Peter and Andrew and James and John. Peter was called the Big Fisherman. A couple of years ago, Lloyd Douglas wrote a best seller called *The Big Fisherman.* Is it because Peter was physically larger than the others? Or did he own a fleet of fishing sloops, or did he acquire the name after his discipleship? At times he is known as Simon, and sometimes as simply 'The Rock.' Jesus taught them all to go fishing for men. So what do you think the best bait is for men, Skip?"

"Beautiful girls and beer, but Jesus didn't use either of those," I grinned. "He promised eternal life. But it's hard to know what that really means when you're still living here." I tried to speak normally, but my breath was coming hard and fast. My arms ached all the way up to my skull. Eddie didn't seem to mind at all as he propelled us forward.

"The devil uses babes and booze, wealth and fame, and every other temptation known to man," Frank said. "Isn't it interesting, Alcoholics Anonymous and religions draw people by attraction, not by advertising."

It was just light enough to imagine us on the Sea Of Galilee, three brothers rowing out to load the boat. The black dory balanced perfectly as we sped forward. I saw with pride that we left a white, bubbling wake at our stern and I wondered what the horsepower would be if we translated Eddie's muscle to an outboard motor.

"Christ is the perfect example of a real leader," Frank continued. "The first one to step forward, the one to put the most at risk, and his people followed him literally into the valley of death. This is the way life should be lived, in exploration, close to the edge, with a large brilliant flame, or not at all. Screw all the little stuff in between." Once Frank settled into this kind of groove, all subjects were fuel to the conflagration. "The Vikings, Pilgrims, Grand Banks fishermen and the taxis in Venice all used oars. Fifty years ago rowboats were to a family what the car is today. They were used for business, recreation–the most efficient way to get from here to there. Occasionally they used sails in a fair wind, but oars exactly like these were used when it really counted. Beautiful pieces of ash. Never oak or pine or maple. Only ash."

I tried not to be obvious about gulping in air, and managed to say, "I thought about attaching a bow ram on the front of this boat, like the Greek war ships, but I decided it was too much of an inconvenience."

"You'd be the only battle wagon in Plymouth capable of a direct assault."

"I could have every six-foot dinghy in the harbor begging for mercy. Feared tyrant of every bathtub in sight, as long as they couldn't row faster than me." *Breathe! Breathe!* "Let's put one on the *Stanley* and we'll terrorize rich yachts the same way pirates did. Attack only those capable of paying a king's ransom for their safe return to shore."

"Great thought," Eddie said, leaning a little harder into the oars. He wasn't even winded.

Frank agreed. "All those rich, fat asses and their comely young maidens petitioning us for clemency, imploring us to accept their fortunes and spare their mundane lives. We'll move the *Stanley* to Monaco and hang out with princes."

We were moving like the wind! I pictured my young lungs and my fifteen-year old heart exploding. I knew Eddie would have slowed down a little if I asked, but asking was even harder than breathing.

"I'd like to row one of those racing sculls the college kids use," Eddie said.

"They're splendid examples of fast, light wooden boats," Frank nodded. "You know they've got moving seats, allowing for a greater reach. The Greeks accomplished the same thing by greasing the pants of the rowers." He squinted in the soft, semi-light of pre-dawn and pointed at another figure on the sea. "Who's that?"

"Honey Gaspar," I answered. "Wonder if he's been here all night?"

"All night?" Eddie repeated. "You think?"

"Maybe. He's one of the serious scholars of striper fishing." I was tempted to follow him, but decided it would be better to land at least one decent striped bass on my own. If the Cordage Channel proved unproductive, my backup plans included fishing the Gooseneck, the old coal barge wreck or the Cow Yard.

"I don't know him," Frank said. "What's he like?"

"Good guy. Passionate about fishing."

Honey had an unyielding mistress, a life-long love affair with stripers. His siren called most seductively on soft summer evenings when large fish prowled, searching the dark, wet channels for eels, squid, tinker mackerel, small lobsters or pogeys. He cherished bass, the larger the better. Pretending we might be in a good spot, I stopped rowing. To my relief, Eddie did too. He and Frank looked at Honey, then back at me. "Funny thing about poor Honey," I said. "All he wants to talk about is stripers, but he can't reveal his secret places. Doesn't leave much to say, especially since that's all anyone wants to know."

"He talks to you though," Frank said. "I can tell."

"Yeah. He trusts me not to tell his secrets. And he's taught me a lot."

"Like what?"

"Like the way stripers cut line with their gills. And how important it is to wash my hands before touching the bait. How to use chum. Lots of tips about stripers. Did you know that stripers have four nasal passages?"

"As a matter of fact, no," said Frank. "But now I do."

My arms were burning, but my breathing had returned to normal. "Let's start rigging up the eels. We want to be ready when we hit the channel." Could they see my hands shaking? Probably too dark to see me fumbling with the large silver hook and the slippery eels. With the expectant light just before dawn, the tide began to run out with authority. I took an extra deep breath to relax and caught the distinct aroma of sweet, salty sardines in the air, the perfume of promise.

Frank steered us out to a red buoy at the junction of the Kingston Cuts and the Cordage Channel. Somebody was in the Cow Yard, but we were alone heading in the channel.

It may have been a holiday for Frank and Eddie, but it was a serious workday for me. I had never made a bad trip on the *Stanley*. Frank and Eddie always found the fish. "Water's pretty calm," I commented. "Better if the surface ripples. Stripers get spooky with glassy conditions." I tossed the first line overboard. "Come on, fish! Jump right in this little boat. Come on, come on."

Fish seem most elusive when you are in the greatest need. When you absolutely must find them, they disappear. It would be so embarrassing if we returned without catching a single one. "There are so many fish here we may have to hide while we bait these hooks," I joked nervously. "Be careful, we don't want anyone knocked overboard."

Eddie pretended to duck. He and Frank laughed quietly.

"Eddie, take the white rod with the worm and fish the port side. Frank, use the eels, starboard side, and pay out line slowly until you have 40 or 50 fifty feet out. After I make the left turn, let out another 10 or 20 feet." The role reversal felt awkward in a strangely pleasant way. I knew my directions were correct, my authority temporary.

I started to row against the outgoing tide, wishing I hadn't tried so hard to keep up with Eddie. Should have faked it a little, I'd be less tired. "Rocky Nook is straight ahead. Three hundred yards, then I'll turn left for the Cordage chimney."

"Oh, okay." I heard the smile in Frank's voice, and realized he'd forgotten our primary purpose. With his pole anchored under his arm, he lit a cigarette. I longed for one myself, but what I really wanted was a linesider on the hook.

Eddie's line rested on top of his left index finger and under his thumb as he watched the water. "Come on fish, let's *go*."

"Welcome the child of morning," Frank said. "Ahhhh, the rosy fingers of Dawn. Why do we rely on excuses like work or fishing to get up early enough to see sights like this? Why don't we just set the alarm and appreciate nature's gift?"

"Ha," I said, "right." *It's getting light, that means it's getting late. Come on fish!* Not a single bird in sight. A bad sign. It's possible to have a good fishing day and never see a bird, but it's reassuring to see them feeding. On extremely rare occasions I spotted baitfish on top of the water before the gulls, and I took great pride in beating the ever-vigilant gulls at their own game. My stomach knotted. *Come on ... come on!*

"God this is great. I never get to relax like this," Frank said, and at that moment, I realized it was ridiculous to worry. It wasn't going to matter to them if we caught fish or not. This was a day off, a day to be relished and enjoyed. A day of friendship and conversation.

Finally, a subtle swirl on the flat, shiny surface. Eddie tensed, ready for a strike. "I feel like a passenger on the *Louise*!" He stood up. "Open wide, wider please. You'll feel a little pin-prick. Now swallow. Doctor Eddie is going to clean your big, beautiful teeth."

Frank could not see the fish, sitting in the stern seat facing forward, away from the baited lines. As the comfortable, non-rowing seat, the aft thwart in a dory is referred to as the "easy chair." Frank was watching Eddie and didn't see the line on his own rod lose its gentle arc into the water. Three things could cause this–the line had snagged seaweed or other debris, the eel had sensed danger and was swimming with added vigor or a bass had inhaled the eel and would feel the hook any moment now. Suddenly the reel slipped out of Frank's grip and hit the edge of the boat. Lightning quick, he snatched it up. The reel screeched, singing its high-pitched song of success.

"You got a bass!" I told him. "A big mother!"

"Wha-hoo!" said Frank. "I got a freight train here!"

"Tighten up the drag, he's going to empty your reel!" Eddie said, but I knew the fish would slow down before the line ran out. As I would have for any other fishing party, I'd set the drags on all the reels with enough tension to tire a large bass, but not so much as to rip out the hook or break the line.

"Come on, come on!" Frank's favorite fishing sweater, the one with several small moth holes, made him look like the quintessential fisherman. Spitting out his cigarette so he could use both hands, gently, firmly, he guided the fish toward the dory. She rolled on the surface; silver, highly polished mirrors, reflecting every color in soul-cleansing beauty, resplendent in the new sun. Diamonds, not scales; pure light, brighter than its source, sharing its radiance with us. As Frank brought the fish closer to the boat, each run became shorter than the last. I gaffed it cleanly, near the head, and removed the hook for him, just as I would on the party boat.

"God, that was fun! That really was the cat's ass!" Frank exclaimed.

I held her up, an 18 pound, fat, female. The kind of fish you could leave conspicuously on the float a few extra minutes as you unloaded the dory. "Ladies and gentlemen, please say Hello to the new Miss Massachusetts!"

I watched their faces, heard their laughter, felt their joy. No pressures to produce. No concerns regarding the price at the dock.

"This is as good as it will ever be," Frank said. "We will never have a world better than it is right now. Wars will become ever more destructive, more pollution, more crime, a few very rich and more starving poor. We need to take pleasure from every day, no matter what it brings. Especially enjoy days like today and remember their sweetness."

Eddie had been slowly reeling in his line to avoid a tangle with Frank's fish. Suddenly his rod bent over in a beautiful arc. He gripped my stiff bass rod, more like a cue stick than a fishing rod.

Now Frank gave animated advice: "Eddie, you've got a fine, fine, fish there. Don't horse him too hard. You may have three or four more runs before he's next to the boat."

As we whooped encouragement, Eddie landed a 25-pound striper. He turned to me. "Finest kind, Cap't.! Finest kind!"

"Let's give our Captain a break, I'm gonna row," Frank said, giddy with success.

Once again, the dory cut smartly through the water, Frank headed us straight for the tall brick Cordage chimney.

As we approached, we saw a guard standing in the middle of the wharf watching us. By the time we were fifty yards away, two more guards appeared.

Eddie's rod twitched and he hooked onto another smaller bass. I gaffed it into the boat and held it up to our audience. We were 25 yards away now. A guard yelled out, "Nice fish!"

"Want it?" I hollered back.

"No. Thanks, anyway."

"Gung ho bastard," Eddie whispered.

"One of them has a side arm," Frank said. "Looks like a .38."

The first guard looked mellow as he vicariously enjoyed the fishing. When the others arrived, they all acted more menacing, arms akimbo, legs apart, looking out over the water at us, directly into the sun. Two already had on dark sunglasses, and all of them wore the visors of their hats low on their foreheads. They looked tall and fit from our angle down in the water.

"Let's cruise around and look at both sides of the wharf," Frank suggested quietly.

We maintained our facade of fishing, catching some schoolies that were too small to keep.

"Let's use an eel. Looks like diaper stripers or snapper blues are picking off the tails of our worms," I said.

"Okay." Eddie jerked the rod back to set the hook, missed, and slipped backward. He had not fully regained his balance when another fish took the hook with a sledgehammer blow. Eddie had the star-drag cranked down to its max. Show no mercy, take no prisoners! The tight, unyielding reel gave no slack and the fish went straight up, two feet into the air. A beautiful bluefish shimmered in the dawn.

"I'm in love!" I said. In a perfect world I'd fish for blues during the day and stripers at night, but a good year for stripers means a poor season for blues, and vice versa. Stripers grow much larger, up to 75 pounds, while a large blue weighs in at about 20. After setting the hook a striper typically makes a long, straight run, rarely breaking the surface, with each successive run becoming shorter until the fish sees the boat. Blues are more erratic and muscular, often surging to the surface, slapping white water all around them, like this one.

"Haul him in, the faster the better," I said to Eddie. "Don't give him a chance to chew through the leader. I don't have any wire on the boat."

I was thankful that it was on a single hook. A fresh blue flapping around in a narrow dory with treble hooks and chomping jaws can be dangerous. My guess is that bluefish send more people to the hospital for hook removal than any other species. As the fish saw my hand approaching it snapped vigorously at my fingers. “I can tap it on the head, but first, take a look at the eyes.”

Eddie and Frank both leaned forward to see. The bluefish glared at us, fierce, vengeful, disconcertingly unafraid, the eyes yellow-orange with large black pupils. I heard they could look in a different direction with each eye, forward with the right and backward with the other, but I never held one long enough to find out for sure.

“They’re like suns, alive, fiery and charged with the energy of life,” Frank said. And like a brilliant sunset we knew the light would soon be gone.

“Bluefish are the piranhas of the north,” Eddie said. “You fall overboard into a school, your skeleton would be stripped clean in about a minute. Worse than piranhas.”

I pointed to a spot by the blue’s pectoral fin. “Look at this, it’s larger and brighter than normal. A clear signal she’s sexually mature.”

“Those are beautiful fish, Skip. Let’s do this again,” Frank said. He lifted his cap, revealing the never-tanned area of his head. “I can’t remember the last time I just sat and enjoyed myself.”

“It helps to be lucky, I’m glad we caught a few,” I said, pleased.

“I used to know an old skipper in Gloucester who always said, *When you leave the dock, you give your boat, your net and your life to God*,” Eddie said. “If you’re lucky, He gives them all back to you with a few fish thrown in as a gift. But what are we going to do about those stinking guards?”

“Let’s see what else we can find out about them.” Frank lit a cigarette and took a long drag.

“Rolly said he was going to ask his friend,” I reminded them. “Maybe he knows what to do.”

“We need to know if they ever use those guns, or if they’re just for show.” Eddie admired his fish. “Just like a woman, aching to be caught,” he grinned.

The next morning we met with Rolly and Troy in the fo’castle and told them about all the guards.

Rolly nodded. “Yeah, that’s what I found out. That place is tighter than a crab’s ass. My contact said it would take an atom bomb to get in, and even then you might not get the money.”

“All kinds of guards around, especially on pay day,” Troy put in.

"Brinks guards plus the regular Cordage guards." My plans to be idle and rich were slipping away. "Sounds like we need machine guns and bazookas."

We talked about it all day. Frank kept asking if anyone had come up with any thoughts, and no one did. Finally he said, "It was a good idea, but we need to face the facts. This isn't going to happen. There's enough fear, injury, and killing that takes place in this world by accident or design, without us adding to the slaughter. Cheating the government out of a few import tax dollars is not a problem for me. Walking in with guns, blasting everybody, is a different category altogether."

Everyone nodded, filled with mixed emotions. As eager as we were to take money from a rich, anonymous company, I sensed a collective sigh of relief.

Waiting for ice after unloading another three-day trip, I walked over to the Esso station, the only source of gas and diesel fuel for commercial boats in Plymouth. I really liked Vic Correia, the owner, even though he always called me Dickey.

The previous year I had walked into his gas station early on Christmas Eve. It looked like college kids jammed into a phone booth, local fishermen shoulder to shoulder in his tiny office. The temperature inside felt like 105 despite the chill outside. Next to the cash register sat a large, half empty bottle of Seagram's Seven.

Vic pushed through the noisy crowd and shook my hand. "Merry Christmas Dickey!" he said.

"Merry Christmas, Vic!" A paper cup appeared in my hand. I took a sip and choked.

Through my winter coat I felt Sal Salucchi's strong hand patting my back. "*Ayyy, Wallahoo*, Come on!" he called. "*Ma sei pazzo*? Put some ginger ale in here. You trying to get me drunk?" The cup came back full as he passed it to me. I took a very small taste and smiled. Mostly ginger ale. "Thanks, Sal. Got plans for Christmas?"

"Yeah. Gonna play Santa to the nieces and nephews. I've done it the past three years, but the older ones, they get suspicious. Most of it I do in Italian and I almost never talk Italian around them. Anyway, I can't get too drunk or they'll know who the hell I am." Sal drained his cup in one gulp. "After that we'll have some nice pasta, sardines, some wine and then go to the midnight. You know where I live, come by."

But today Christmas felt remote as I stood sweating from the blistering summer sun. There is nothing like hot, humid air to intensify the smells of two-day-old lobster bait and yesterday's gurry. I picked up a quart of ice cream, asked Vic to charge it, and devoured it before I reached the edge of the pier. The heat had driven everyone from town down to the edge of the water.

Jerry Cardose sat on a fish box waiting for the *Carlansul* to start unloading. He had a cleft palate and one of the worst lisps in town. "Hey Kip, how'th the ballth of your feet?" he said.

"Hey, Cardose, Fahla eengglesh?"

"No, no, never."

He gave me a playful punch to the stomach, "Careful, you might hurt your hand," I said.

Frank caught up with me after paying Vic. "Hey Jerry, you dried out yet?"

"Dried out but I can't get rid of the thmell!"

They roared at the in-joke, then Frank turned to me. "I bought Jerry a drink last night, and he told me about a lonely old man who died in the Brick Block. On the top floor, above Eddie and those other fishermen he bunks with. The stairway is steep and narrow on that last flight and it's impossible to get a stretcher up there." Frank wiped his forehead and shook his head. "Poor old guy must have been dying for some time because he was just bones with damned little skin over his emaciated ass. Maybe he starved to death–never any visitors up there. Anyway, the undertaker calls Jerry to help him with this job."

You could see Jerry's muscles ripple, even when he was relaxed, lighting up a cigarette. He carried a pack of Camels rolled up in the left sleeve of his ultra-white T-shirts. I was thin and strong too, but for some reason my muscles never stood out like his or Frank's or Eddie's. I had tried lifting weights and rubbing olive oil on my skin. Nothing worked.

"Jerry walks up to the room and the undertaker tries to help him," Frank went on, "but the stairs are too confining..."

Jerry took up the story: "Tho I thed, 'Thtand over there. I can carry him alone. I juth need to get him up on my thoulder...'"

Frank interrupted, "So Jerry gives him a heave onto his right shoulder and gets to the second step... and suddenly he feels his back getting wet."

I made a face. “Oh no...”

“Jerry throws him off and runs down the stairs, screaming ‘You thun of a bith! If you can pith, you can walk! I ain’t carrying nobody who is pithing down my freaking back!”

It pleased Frank that Jerry had walked into the Bird before changing shirts. It lent an air of heightened reality to Jerry’s narrative. People were buying Jerry drinks–everyone having a good time, when things got out of control. Somebody spilled a beer down Jerry’s back. Frank wasn’t sure if it was an accident, but the police didn’t care. One guy was still in Jordan Hospital a week later.

Trouble With The Law

Women, can't live with 'em... Can't shoot 'em.

Ivan Turgenev, *Quotes*

When Eddie asked if he could move his stuff onto the *Stanley*, we knew his marriage was on the rocks. For weeks he'd been complaining that he dreaded going home, and preferred to meet his daughter at Ernie's Restaurant, at school or other public places. "Hell's Bells," he said, "every penny I earn goes to that ball buster of a wife. The bitch has peanut butter legs."

Frank laughed, then caught my puzzled glance. "He means she's always got a pair of nuts between them."

"Oh."

"So, is it okay with you, Capt.?"

"Sure. Sorry about the circumstances, Old Dog."

"Not half as sorry as me."

He decided to sleep in the pilothouse bunk, which was larger and better ventilated than those in the fo'castle. On the first night his nose helped him track down an old peach pie and a dozen donuts in various stages of decay.

"Oh," I said when he showed me the next day. "I think Troy was looking for those!"

Eddie also discovered my rifle, which I kept under the mattress to protect it from the salt air. Not inclined to sleep with it, he hung it on the wall, giving the bunk the distinct look of a Texas pickup truck.

The next day the phone rang at 3:15 a.m. just as I was getting ready to leave the house.

"We're going to be delayed this morning," Frank said. "Be at the boat around eight and I'll fill everyone in then." *Click.*

My mother ran out of her room. "Who died? Where's your brother?"

"No one," I said. I went back to bed, but couldn't sleep, and wound up just lying there until about 7:30. I got to the *Stanley* at 7:45, and everyone was there except Eddie. *Uh oh.* I looked at Frank questioningly.

"He's at the police station. I guess they had a wild time down here last night."

"What happened?"

"Big fight with the wife, then Eddie went to the Bird, had a couple of brews and came down to the boat. He was asleep but woke up when he heard a noise."

"What kind of noise?"

"The kind of noise the dock lines make when someone throws them into the water."

"*What*?"

"The *Stanley* starts to move away from the dock and Eddie runs out and sees his wife standing there. He's so mad that he grabbed your rifle and started shooting. Not to hit her, just to scare her away."

"Poor Eddie!"

"Poor Eddie is right. He no sooner starts the gas kicker going and maneuvers the boat back to its berth, when a coupla cops arrive full of questions."

"Shit."

Frank's gaze wandered past me, and I saw annoyance in his eyes. He muttered, "I was afraid of this."

Turning around, I saw two cops headed for us. My stomach turned over when I saw one was carrying my rifle. Frank stood a little straighter and greeted them cordially.

"Who is the owner of this rifle," the cop demanded. He had small white flecks at the corners of his mouth and I couldn't tell if they were saliva or the remains of his last sugar donut.

"Me," I said.

"Why's it on the boat?"

"We shoot sharks with it."

He glared. It was not a weapon designed to kill sharks and we both knew it. I took a cue from Frank and stood without flinching. "Gimme your name and address," he ordered, and when I complied, he smirked, "You the kid that killed the whale." It was not a question.

"I'm the one that tried to *save* the whale." I stopped short of adding *you asshole*. I felt Frank step a little closer to me. I was glad to see the other cop was Sergeant Zuchelli, one of the few decent cops on the force. He told me they'd need to keep my rifle as evidence.

"Okay." I made myself sound submissive. Like most small towns,

Plymouth had a police force that tended to round up the usual suspects anytime something bad happened. Unfortunately I was one of them, not without reason.

Several years earlier I smacked a baseball through an old lady's window. No one was home, so I walked in, picked up the ball and the game continued. When the old lady got home she saw the broken glass and called the police. She couldn't find her favorite Bible, and she told them someone had broken in and stolen it. One of the other baseball players informed the police and the next day a policeman walked into our class and told the teacher he wanted me to go with him to the station.

I wasn't afraid of him. I had already told my mother, whom I was afraid of. A stint in jail didn't scare me at all.

"Say goodbye to freedom, kid," the cop said. "You'll probably wind up in reform school. You got a record now, that means no one will hire you. That means you'll be broke and you'll have to rob innocent people to survive. You'll probably spend the rest of your life in prison or on the run."

Okay, now I was paying attention.

But right after he shoved me into a chair, Sergeant Zuchelli walked in, "This kid in trouble?"

"Breaking and entering and stealing a Bible from a little old lady," said the cop, who I had named *Forever Asshole.*

Zuchelli said, "Let's hear your side, Skippy."

I told him what happened, adding, "My mother kept trying to call her and tell her how sorry I was, and that we'd replace the glass, but she couldn't get through."

"Kid swiped her Bible!" Forever Asshole shouted.

"I did not! I didn't touch a thing! I just got the ball and left."

Zuchelli turned to Forever Asshole. "You really think this kid is gonna steal a Bible?"

"Well, I mean–"

"Skippy," said Zuchelli, "get that window fixed today, understand?" To Forever Asshole he said, "And you. Get this kid back to school where he belongs."

As soon as class let out, I went to the lady's house to measure the window. Before I could even apologize, she had milk and homemade chocolate chip cookies on the table.

"Sit and eat," she said. "Your mother called. I found the Bible. I'm sorry I called the police."

"It's okay," I said, "I'm sorry too, I know how it must have looked." Killing innocent whales, stealing Bibles, what was next?

Now, I stared at the rifle. This. This was next.

"But don't worry," Sergeant Zuchelli went on, "you'll get it back right after the trial."

Trial? Although my mother paid only modest attention to newspapers, she certainly would know if I went to court! I tried to imagine potential benefits from this. How would it sound if I said, "I won't be around tomorrow. I've been subpoenaed to testify at the shooting trial..." or did it sound better if I said, "I'll be in court tomorrow, a friend needs help?" Maybe "My rifle was involved in a shooting." Good conversation to impress girls, but my lines needed work. I'd ask Frank about it as soon as we were alone.

The cop who wasn't Zuchelli crouched down and pointed at small pieces of lead in the wooden pilings of the pier. "I'll pry these out, they're evidence," he said.

"You'll have to excuse us," Frank said, politely but suddenly brisk. "You know where to find us if you need us. Come on, Skip."

I followed him down the dock and we drove to the jail. I was shocked when he stepped into view after Frank posted bail. I had seen Eddie many times early in the morning, when he had not slept for days. I'd seen him without a shave, with fish gurry clinging to the stubble of his beard. But I had never seen him with his head hanging low, devoid of pride.

Frank grabbed him into a rough bear hug. "Come on Old Dog, let's go fishing."

Three days later we returned to Plymouth to discover that everybody knew about the shooting. The news was on the radio and in the *Old Colony Memorial*, our weekly newspaper. Most effective of all, local gossips had enlarged the story to operatic proportions. One version sounded like Billy the Kid starring in *Wreck Of The Hesperus*.

"Where is your gun?" asked my mother as soon as I opened the door.

"I'm fine, thanks." Apprehensively, I eyed my father, and wisely kept my mouth shut, as I headed for a bath and clean clothes.

Frank hired the best lawyer in town, and in the ten days prior to the hearing, acted as unofficial legal counsel to Eddie and me.

"Don't volunteer information. If the question can be answered yes or no, your answer will be *Yes, sir* or *No, your honor*. Period. Then wait for the next question. Extra points are given for politeness, but don't get flowery. The shorter your answers, the better. Sometimes lawyers try to stare you down." He leaned toward me and I attempted to follow his instructions. "If a lawyer tries to unsettle you by prolonged eye contact, stare right back, but focus your eyes at a spot in the center of his forehead. That gives the impression of staring him directly in the eyes but it's much easier."

"Okay," Eddie and I said together. It was fascinating to see one more field in which Frank was an expert.

"Remember. Do exactly what I say, and you'll be fine."

I was called as the first witness.

"Is this your .22 rifle?" the lawyer asked. His dark blue suit contrasted with his impeccable white shirt with gold French cuffs. The unmistakable look of money. He walked with military posture and the suit moved with him.

"Yes, sir."

"No further questions. You may step down."

The lawyer had no trouble establishing that Eddie had acted in self-defense. Someone had tried to endanger his livelihood, if not his very life, by casting off the dock lines to the *Stanley*. It had been too dark to see the villain (or villainess) who, with malice aforethought, tried to damage a boat, worth thousands of dollars, owned by Captain Francis Savery. This cowardly act, perpetrated on a moonless night, demanded, no, *required*! the strong, vigorous response of firing a small rifle. Edward Fairweather was an excellent marksman and could easily have wounded his assailant had that been his intention. His prompt action may have prevented further vandalism to other innocents.

The judge heard both sides, banged his gavel, and ruled in favor of the defense. There was no mention of the rumor that Eddie invited a young lady for a midnight tour of our fascinating fishing vessel.

Frank in his Army uniform, circa 1922.

Skip at the wheel of the *Louise*.

Eddie with the Great White Shark he caught.

The *Louise* about to leave the dock.

Skip fishing with a hand line on the *Louise*.

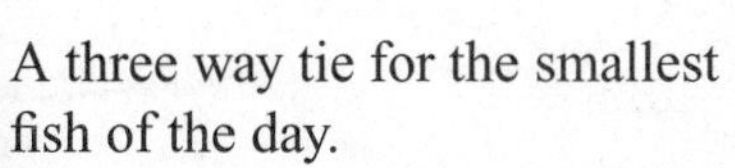

A three way tie for the smallest fish of the day.

This tame 11-foot porpoise, driven ashore Tuesday morning at Town Brook then dragged over in front of Plymouth Rock where it was viewed by hundreds of curious visitors. It died late Tuesday afternoon after battering itself against the rocks in the inner harbor south of Winter stret and must now be buried by the owner of the shore land on which it beached, the Townsend property on Warren avenue.

The species, a "common porpoise," was spotted in the inner harbor by Charles Rose and George Monks, two local boat owners and was driven into the mouth of Town Brook where a rop wase placed about its tail. Taking part in the capture besides Rose and Monks were Jackie Morey and Dexter DeBrusk. The mammal was dragged into deep water with the afternoon tide and swam away but it was later learned that it had died and come ashore below Winter street.

Belief that the mammal was tame is based on the fact of a healed-over carving "TYD-32."

Newspaper photo from the Old Colony Memorial showing Skip (far right) and Charlie Rose (2nd from right) with pilot whale (incorrectly stated in article as a porpoise).

Frank looking tanned and lean.

Eddie at sea.

Frank looking out the wheel-house window of the *Stanley*. (Note missing fingers.)

Skip waiting to disconnect the 500 pound otter board from the main towing cable.

The full net coming over the rail. There's a full cowhide used as chafing gear to protect the twine on the right side of the net.

The net is so full it requires "splitting" into sections in order to haul the fish aboard.

Frank steadies the net while Skip reaches for the pucker strings.

Eddie and Frank emptying the net. The cutting box is on the left.

Steaking whiting. Rolly and Eddie cutting heads.

Frank takes a careful look at the twine.

The tuna Skip harpooned on the *Frances Elizabeth.*

The Lightship *Nantucket*.

Skip's house circa 1940. The house his grandfather built, his Mother was born in and he grew up in.

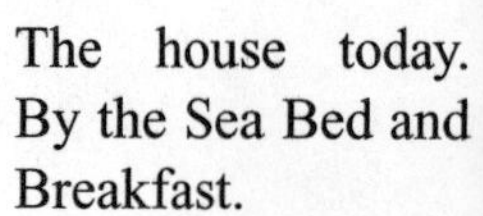
The house today. By the Sea Bed and Breakfast.

Frank and his wife outside their home.

Captain Stan "Pat" Burgess in front of the Plymouth Fish Pier today.

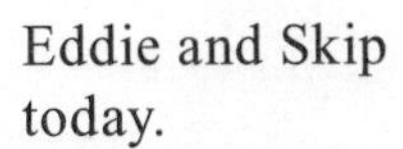

Eddie and Skip today.

Shark Tales

Fishing simply sent me out of my mind. I could neither think nor talk of anything else, so that my mother was angry and said she would not let me fish again because I might fall ill from such excitement.

Sergei Aksarov, *Memoir*

It felt good to leave Plymouth as far away as possible, and during our trip to Nantucket Shoals I learned another difference between fishing for fun and fishing for a living. It would take a huge amount of fish to pay our fuel bill. We were on sandy bottom, holding to a fifteen-fathom line. The net had been down less than twenty minutes. The wire cables crackled as I steered them evenly onto the winch drum, humming with the heavy-laden vibration of a full net. It would require at least two splits before we brought the bag on board.

"Great haul!" beamed Eddie.

But our excitement disappeared when we saw the net overflowing, not with cod or lemon sole, but dogfish.

"Satanic, spiny, shit-sucking sharks!" Frank shouted. "Syphilitic sons of whores, what a total pain in the posterior. This mess will take hours to clean up."

There'd be no silvery, slippery bodies poured with ease onto the deck. Dogfish spines were stuck in the net, and the high friction of their abrasive hides made a solid, unmovable mass. The most abundant of all the sharks, they average three feet long and travel in large packs like wild dogs, pushing other fish out of an area. Greedy, nasty-tempered scavengers who will eat anything. They have evil eyes, cold and green with a vertical, reptilian slit, which give them a cannibalistic look.

A scientist onboard the *Louise* once taught me how to cut the spines off at their base and count the circular rings to determine a dogfish's age. They are unique among fish in that they give live birth. Mothers average two to ten pups in a litter. When we caught pregnant females on the *Louise*, they would sometimes go into labor because of the trauma of decompression. Baby sharks are born with an egg yolk attached. This benefit allows the young shark a constant supply of food. It can also be life threatening, as it slows down escape from predators. With a serious group of fishermen, I'd instantly hook them as bait. Once a customer used one and caught a 45-five pound cod within minutes. The fish, taller than me, easily won the pool prize for the largest catch. The customer gave me half the money, twelve dollars, an unimaginable amount of money for a boy earning a dollar a day, plus tips.

On our next trip there was not an eager fisherman in the crowd of pick-up partiers who joined us on a random basis. It was more women than men, which was unusual; just people looking for a break in the historical tours. The first dogfish we caught spewed out little ones all over the deck. I grabbed the nearest hook, impaled a baby, sure that it would translate into another monster cod along with another monster tip.

But life is complicated and not easy to predict. The woman whose hook I'd baited blew her stack! Swearing ferociously, she could have given truck drivers lessons. By the time she finished, you'd think I was solely responsible for every war crime and human atrocity ever committed. Logic didn't help. Reason did not prevail. The potential for enormous cod held zero appeal. The idea of cashing in on a pool was too bourgeois to merit discussion. With true remorse, I threw the cute little babies over the stern, shaking my head with genuine regret as the totally defenseless pups towed their lunch box yolks slowly away from the *Louise*. Fifteen feet away, they became Epicurean *hors d'oeuvres* for the insatiable sea gulls.

I flipped the dumb broad a mental pigeon. Actually, I delivered a dozen, one for each of the wasted baits and a few extra for good luck. Screw her!

Revenge felt sweet, very sweet indeed, when it came. The next fish on her line was a big female shark. She didn't know what to do with the creature as it thrashed in the water. The one-pound lead sinker clanked into the side of the boat chipping off white paint.

"Yours," I said to Charlie and walked away. He had the fish off in seconds. The woman stopped fishing and went up to the forward deck, vigorously applying suntan lotion.

Charlie moved his hand to his head and then to his buttocks and smiled. No brains, big ass.

I smiled and returned to shucking razor clams, nice safe bivalve mollusks for bait. An hour later, I went forward to pull the anchor, and while we moved to the next location I felt her eyes directly on my back. I looked at her and held her stare without wavering. Ready for her. Unexpectedly, she smiled. "I'm sorry I was so unkind back there."

I tried to look busy, nodded briskly.

"You love doing this, don't you?"

"Mmm."

"I'm a long way from home." When I didn't ask how far, she said, "I'm from Minnesota. I grew up on a soybean farm. Have you ever heard of such a thing?"

I shook my head, reluctantly interested. "Is that what you do for a living, you're a soy bean farmer?"

"No. I teach high school."

No wonder I didn't like her! "Math?"

"English. I'm also the wrestling coach."

"Boy's wrestling?"

"Yes, since there isn't a girl's team. We were 8 and 0 last year. We had a couple of guys like you–skin, bones and muscle."

"Good record," I said, but mostly I was flattered by the compliment.

"Have you read Hemingway yet?"

"Only *For Whom The Bell Tolls*."

"You know, Papa Hemingway is an avid fisherman. I think he loves fish, really big fish, almost as much as you do. He goes fishing all the time–Key West, Cuba. He also wrote a short story called 'Hills Like White Elephants.' Have you read it?"

"Not yet."

"Usually they don't teach this until college, but you might enjoy it. Do you know what an abortion is?"

I wasn't clear on all the details, it wasn't something I had ever heard anyone talk about *ever*. "Well–sure," I answered cautiously. We were alone. No one else could hear our conversation on the foredeck. "Why do you ask?"

"I had one. Exactly a year ago today. Eleven o'clock in the morning. My baby didn't nourish anything except an overblown ego. Seeing those primitive sharks, survivors of every calamity on earth, being used as bait just really, well, it really upset me. I thought I was going to get sick. All I could think about was..." she gestured, eyes suddenly wet.

"Only one or two per cent survive under the best of conditions," I said to make her feel better.

Her turn to nod. Neither of us spoke for several minutes, then she said, "What's your favorite sea story?"

Out of the corner of my eye I saw a client having trouble with a medium-sized cod he'd just caught; the thing was flipping around and he wasn't able to grip it long enough to take it off the hook. But I couldn't bring myself to leave. What a horror show this day had been for her! Thinking she was going to take pleasure cruise away from her memories, only to see a writhing, bloody reminder of what happened a year ago! I smiled leisurely, at her service.

"I have a lot of them, some true–do you know about the Royal Tar?"

"No, but I'd like to hear it if you have the time."

Charlie motioned me over, but like a major league pitcher, I shook off the call. "It's about a shipwrecked elephant."

She was able to smile too. "I've never heard of an elephant on any boat except Noah's Ark." Her laugh was musical, girlish. I pictured her in T-shirt, shorts and a shiny metal whistle around her neck. It took a little more work to see her demonstrating a half nelson on a teen-age boy, but something told me I would have signed up for the team.

"In the mid 1830s, there was a traveling circus in Eastern Canada," I said. "At the end of the season, they boarded a steamer heading for Maine. The production consisted of Dexter's Locomotive Museum and Burgess' Collection of Serpents and Birds. There was a brass band, horses, camels, Mogul the elephant, lions, tigers and other assorted animals."

"What fun!"

"Well, not exactly. It was a rough trip. The ship ran for shelter several times. A fire broke out and there was no way to escape except into the water. The elephant decided to jump and landed squarely on some men who were trying to swim away. The bodies of the men and the elephant washed up on the local beach several days later. None of the circus animals survived. There were 93 people on board, 32 died." I looked down at my sneakers. *Stupid jerk! Why tell her such a morbid story?*

She placed her hand firmly on my arm, and her eyes shone; sad, gentle, and grateful. "Oh, that's tragic. Papa Hemingway would love that story."

"I wonder if he knows it?

"I wonder too."

At the same time, we looked at the ocean. Huge, powerful, bigger than anything we could ever do; good or bad. Vast, indifferent.

"You have work to do," she said.

"Yeah, kinda."

"I'll stay here. Work on my tan."

I'll be watching. "Okay."

"Maybe you'll go home tonight and tell your mother you're going to move to Minnesota and join a wrestling team."

With a smile I tried to return to the rest of the customers, and tried to concentrate on clams and codfish. A few times we shared glances. I was honored that she'd shared such a deep and profound secret with me.

At the end of the day, she returned to our main deck and I reached out to help her around the narrow passageway. The sun had transformed her! She'd lost weight, at least 30 pounds, and her grip felt strong but electrically feminine. I would have known it was a female touch if it had been the blackest of nights. I'd heard adults speak of the chemistry between two people, but this was an arresting signal, two acrobats holding on to each other in mid-air. I felt her life force in my hand, on my arm, and knew she drank in mine. I wondered what it would be like to have her as a teacher, and then, without a pause, I wondered what it would be like to kiss her. Slowly, we let each other go. I was sorry, very sorry, to see her leave.

"Damn them doggies," Eddie shouted, pronouncing it with a comical southern drawl: *Dow-geez*. "Cut 'em loose, Frank?"

Frank stepped onto the listing deck to survey the goat's nest. "Go ahead, but hurry! There's no damn choice, we'll never get the net in unless you do." Water sloshed in the scuppers and over the gunnels. "Rolly, ease off! We've too much tension on our lifting tackle." With each wave we heard the *Stanley* strain and creak under the inescapable weight.

I watched as Eddie took several precious minutes to sharpen one of our steaking knives and lashed it onto the handle of our eight-foot boat hook. He stood astride the rail, holding on with only his knees. Reaching out to the top of the net, he cut the twine in large, straight swoops. Slowly, the wave and tide motion moved the dead or stunned fish out of the ragged holes.

The rest of us hauled shreds of net into the boat. It was slow hauling. Dogfish remained stuck by their spines in much of the twine. In our frantic haste to free the net, the spines found their way into our hands, wrists and forearms. The wind started to run against the tide, causing a steep, breaking sea that drenched all of us.

Eddie told Rolly to pass him the gilson line with a lot of slack and then tried unsuccessfully to pass it around the swollen net. The effort exhausted him. "Here, Skip, catch!" Leaning out, he gave the coiled line a shoulder pitch. I caught the hook, but to my horror, he fell into the water.

"Oh shit!" Instantly Frank jumped out of the wheelhouse and reached down to grab Eddie's arm. Troy grabbed the other arm, and they hauled him back into the boat.

"God, that felt good. I'm wide awake now," Eddie said.

Shock, panic, and then relief as the choppy, vertical seas kept him close to the boat and the weight of the overstuffed net slowed down our drift. If it had happened in January, it could have been a very different ending.

Eddie changed into dry clothes and climbed back on deck minutes later. We cut both the top and the bottom twine and finally freed the net of spiny dogfish. Blood, slime and guts covered the deck, a stench that overpowered everything else and made us all nauseous. "We're hauling ass out of here, God, what a disgusting mess," Frank said.

For the next hour we mended twine while Frank brought us southeast of Nantucket. He filled twine needles for us as he steered to a new site. No one spoke, and I know we were all thinking how close we'd come to losing Eddie. I didn't know if it was something I could joke about, or be sincere and say how glad I was that he was okay. I kept glancing at him as he silently mended twine.

Troy came up on deck with coffee for us, and I noticed he served Eddie first. "I hung up your bathing suit, Mr. Weissmuller," he said solemnly.

"Make sure it's nice and dry! Nothing I hate worse than getting into a wet bathing suit." Eddie drained his cup in one gulp. "I can't swim a stroke, never could, but you can bet your sweet ass I don't want to learn with those sonuvabitching sharks."

As we laughed, the tension eased, and the brisk damp breeze cleared out the stink of dogfish.

"I thought we were going to get rich quick," Frank sighed.

"Almost as good as the Cordage Company heist. The fish were so thick I could see them on the fathometer. I thought for sure they were codfish. When I felt the weight in the net, I thought this would be a quick, easy trip." We sighed along with him, but I knew what he was thinking, because I was thinking it too, and I was sure every man was thinking it. What really mattered was Eddie's safety.

I remembered a trip on the *Louise* several years ago. Early April, our first fishing party of the year with a freshly painted boat. The *Louise* looked shiny-clean, ready for business. The morning emerged leaden, and my winter coat felt thin. At dead low tide I carried gas down the steep ramp. A frost the previous night gave the ramp a thin coating of invisible ice making it unexpectedly treacherous, and I slipped. Without an ounce of fat on my rear end, I felt the pain all the way into bone. The full five gallons of gas slid down to the bottom and I did the same. It was impossible to stand on the steep incline.

Half an hour later, 20 men showed up on a bus from Worcester, along with 15 cases of beer. Two cases had already been consumed for breakfast on the ride to Plymouth. Their baggage also included a full case of Canadian Club, minus one fifth for flavoring their morning coffee. Thank God I wasn't carrying that when I slipped.

They arrived in good spirits, warm from the bus ride and eager to fish. The serious fishermen in the group brought their own rods and reels. We provided hand lines but when we saw customers with their own gear, we knew we needed to find fish, preferably big fish. Large fish in generous quantities brought people back to our boat.

We had more than enough cod by 2:00, with the wind increasing hourly. The raw, rough day led to several casualties who succumbed to seasickness, aggravated by alcohol. I pulled the anchor and prepared to gut codfish on our way home when I saw Stan, a guy whose friends had proudly introduced as a war hero with a Silver Star and a Purple Heart, crouched over, walking along the bench seats. He reached up, grabbed the vertical roof support, and took a long, steady step off the boat. A clean, deliberate action, taken without the least hesitation.

"Man overboard!" I shouted to Charlie. We had to act fast before hypothermia set in. With rough, 40-degree water, our first attempt would have to succeed. Arriving at the dock with less fish than the other boats is an embarrassment. Arriving with one man missing, unconscious or dead... well, it's something you'd rather not do.

"Stan can't swim!" someone yelled and started to take off their coat.

"Stay in the boat, damn it, stay in the boat!" I tried to hold him back–80 pounds versus 180 pounds–both of us determined. "Two people in the water are twice as bad as one," I screamed. "Help me pick two of the strongest men, and tell everyone else to stay in the boat."

"Okay!"

One overly excited idiot threw our life-ring, missing by a mile.

The passengers were alarmed, then angry as Charlie sped away from Stan. *No, turn around go get him! Go get him!* But when he completed a full power U turn and headed back, everyone understood at the same time that we needed to make a straight-on approach. Frigid green water spilled over the bow. Teeth clenched in concentration, and despite the complications of wind, tide, waves and passenger distractions, Charlie brought us alongside Stan. A perfect maneuver. The three men I recruited did not need instructions. They reached over and, in an expertly coordinated move, dragged Stan out of the water. Even with three big men, it was not easy because he was dead weight and soaking wet.

Everyone cheered until they were hoarse. Slapping each other, they jumped and danced. Charlie and I were no longer the hired help; we became instant heroes. I could feel our unity in my stomach, in my spine; from my head to my toes. A popular war hero, I could not imagine Stan going through World War II and then dying on an innocent fishing trip.

"Stan, how did you stay afloat?" one of his friends asked.

"Some air got trapped under my jacket. Luckily, I had it zipped as high as it could go to keep out the wind. I knew if I started to thrash around I'd lose the bubble." Stan choked a little as he coughed up some water. "Unfortunately, I'm stone cold sober now!"

"Here, Stan, this'll warm you right up." Someone handed him a paper cup three-quarters full of Canadian Club.

I just had to ask. "Where the hell did you think you were going?"

"I thought I was on a bus and I was getting off at my stop," he replied.

Frank's voice interrupted my recollections, as he cursed the fact that he had not brought our back-up net.

"That spare is a whiting net, and it's almost as leaky as this one," Eddie said. "This is better for a gravel bottom and ground fish than the whiting rig." He pointed to a triangular, black fin thirty yards off our starboard quarter.

"Shark?" I asked.

"No, it's an ocean sunfish," Eddie replied. "Not a good sign. It means the water is warm and we're going to see jellyfish."

Ocean sunfish are the largest of all the bony fishes despite their tiny brains. The record was set by a 4,400 pound fish after it damaged a steamer in a collision off Australia. They have small eyes and a beak-like mouth, and their bodies are infested, inside and out, with parasites. In some areas they are called by the Latin designation–*Mola Mola*; elsewhere the name "moon fish" applies because at night large numbers of parasites and other small organisms cling to its slime and emit astounding phosphorescence. As unusual and malformed as it appears in the sunlight, it lights up like a Hollywood starlet at night. They are also one of the few fish that feed on jellyfish, and jellies were definitely not our friends.

Our first tow had a few dogfish, but nothing like the mess we left behind. The first set produced a good mix of ground fish–cod and black back flounders, but also jellyfish, as Eddie had predicted. They were not on the bottom, but as we hauled the net back, we dragged it up through a layer of surface water containing the jellies. Their squishy bodies were plastered all through the meshes. We hauled the net up to the top of the boom, stood under it, and shook it vigorously. This removed the bodies of the jellyfish but caused a rain of irritating tentacles to fall upon the shakers. Wherever a string-like tentacle touched skin, it felt like poison ivy, a burning itch that cried out to be scratched. To protect ourselves, we wore full oilskins, scarves or hoods up to protect our necks and rubber bands over our wrists and ankles.

"Be careful when you take a leak, guys," Eddie said. "This is one of those times you want to wash your hands before you go."

"My god, can you imagine this crud on your groin?" Rolly said. "We better not sit on the rail either, this slime is everywhere."

"I never understood why it's called a jellyfish," I said. "It's not jelly or fish."

"I don't know, but the Artic lion's mane trails tentacles over 100 feet in length," Frank said.

"I hope we don't run into that one!" Several years before I had scooped up three different kinds of jellies in Plymouth Harbor and kept them in an old galvanized pail just to look at them. As much as I enjoyed observing them, I found it confusing to sort out true jellyfish from the look-alikes. I felt better after reading that earlier scientists had also confused the polyps for other animals.

"Not even good for sex," Frank joked. "A female moon jelly produces eggs and holds them in her mouth until a male releases sperm into the water where the female draws in the sperm on her oral arms and tentacles."

We laughed, sorting out the trash fish–skates, dogfish and sculpins–and pitching them overboard. Sadly, everything we touched was doomed. Nothing that landed on deck would swim again because most were compressed by other fish coming into the net after them, and the rapid ascent when we hauled the net to the surface ruptured their air bladders. Also, we handled unwanted fish with picks, and the wounds, while not necessarily lethal, didn't help their chance for survival. Frank, our ever-vigilant safety officer, reminded us to watch out for wolf fish and goose fish, both of which possessed Herculean jaws and sharp teeth capable of penetrating a rubber boot and the tender toes inside. Tenacious by instinct, they hold on until well after death.

"Another thing I never understood," I complained. "Why is it called a goosefish? It looks nothing like a goose."

"A misnomer," Frank answered. "Like the naming of Greenland."

"I wonder who came up with all these crazy names?"

"That's a good question, Skip," Frank said. But I noticed he didn't provide an answer!

"You guys are really dense," Eddie shouted across the deck. "It's that real estate agent on Main Street that sold me my first house."

"Yeah, he probably named New Jersey the Garden State too."

As we worked, the fog settled in a thick, milky presence defying penetration. Frank turned on the deck lights early and they glistened on our oilskins, making the deck as bright as day, but also creating the effect of making a long night seem longer. Jellyfish parts, lubricated by fog, made everything more slippery than usual.

Nevertheless, the fishing was good, with more cod on deck than we could gut from one set to the next.

Frank leaned out the wheelhouse window, trying to see through the fog. Although we had set a buoy, we couldn't make it out until we were on top of it. Frank ran a timed compass course, following a depth line of 32 fathoms, and occasionally checked our loran bearings. The varying strength of the tide as it ebbed and flowed, reversing direction every six hours, complicated everything.

Eddie straightened up, and then bent backwards to ease his muscles. "Hey, Capt., let's steak some whiting tomorrow–at least we could do that standing up."

I looked to make sure he was joking, and was glad to catch his grin.

"I'd rather have gurry sores on my wrists than these god damned jellyfish stingers on my face," Rolly said.

"I must have been in a hurry the last time I took a leak," Troy said, "The jellies have caught me by the balls."

There was more than a grain of truth to all this, but it was offered to Frank to cheer him on. He had us on the fish. His job was to keep us there, while our responsibility was simply to put them in the fish hold and keep them iced down–easy compared to Frank's role.

Occasionally, we heard the foghorns of large freighters or passenger liners passing in the distance. We were on the edge of the shipping lanes in and out of New York City. No immediate danger appeared as long as they stayed on course and we held our current position.

"Hey, Skip, wash up and give me a little break, will you," Frank said.

"I'll be right there." Why me? True, I'd slowed down a little; I usually did after midnight, until I got my second wind. Sure, I knelt down, instead of bending over to rip cod bellies, but this wasn't uncommon. Rolly had just gone below on his off watch. Why hadn't Frank asked Eddie to relieve him at the wheel?

I stepped into the small wheelhouse. From the putrid stench of burning flesh, I knew one of his cigarettes had burned too close to a finger stump again.

"I need to give up these damned weeds, but not tonight," Frank said. "We'll run out of ice and be low on food by noon tomorrow. What do you think of going into New York to sell our fish?"

"Might be a little tricky with all this fog," I said.

"What about Hyannis or New Bedford?"

"New Bedford will give us the best price," I answered before I realized he had wanted me to analyze our best options. I'd given him a cliché for an answer when he wanted me to think.

"What about Nantucket?"

Damn! Nantucket never entered my mind. Just because I'd never been there was no excuse. Exactly the opposite, I wished I'd offered it as an option. I was yearning to visit this historic home of whaling and seafaring adventures. "Will they rob us on the price?" I asked, trying to redeem myself.

"Yes, but I've called the buyer and it's better than I thought," he said. "We wasted a full day and a half on those sharks and getting ourselves onto some decent fish. I think our best bet is to run into the closest port, sell what we have and haul ass back out here as quickly as we can. What do you think?"

"What about the price of fuel and food?" I asked. I was wide-awake now, and I knew everything on the island was more expensive than the mainland.

Frank smiled. "We'll take a hit. No doubt about that. Figure out how much it will cost us in fuel to run into the closest port and what the difference is to steam to New Bedford."

"Right now?"

"Why not?"

"It may take me a little time."

"Don't take forever, the cod are ass deep on deck."

Through several mistakes and with Frank's prodding, I stumbled and bumbled to an accurate figure.

"When you get back in school remember tonight," Frank said. "Think how much easier it is to do homework at one o'clock in the afternoon in a study hall than at one in the morning out here. And don't be surprised if I show up some afternoon to check it over."

Nantucket looked even more beautiful than I imagined, gorgeous in a classic way. Provincetown smelled of onions and hot sausages, Plymouth had the scent of beach roses and taffy, while Nantucket smelled of money. I wondered if it smelled the same in winter after all the tourists moved back to New York and Boston.

In the past, Nantucket had been the whaling center of the world.

Whale products were used for nearly everything at the beginning of the industrial age. From lighting to lubrication, sashimi to shoe horns, whale goods were omnipresent. Women's fashions depended on baleen for corsets and stays to accentuate breasts and hips. Baleen was the plastic of the times. Oils and other by-products were used for items ranging from cat food to state-of-the-art-medications. For piano keys and paint, the whale was not just desirable, but necessary.

We scrubbed down the *Stanley* inside and out, and then washed the deck and fish hold a second time. Since the boat would be our home until we returned to Plymouth, we wanted to be sure that all traces of the irritating jellyfish disappeared.

I had finished putting away our groceries when Eddie returned from his reconnaissance trip and announced, "Good news, people. We can stay right here at the dock and the whole damn town will come to us. A band plays here every Saturday night, right at the foot of Main Street. There's music, dancing, and it's free. I picked up a case of beer and the package store is open until 10:00 if we want more."

Yippee! A night off, and with beer and free entertainment! Troy fried chicken, and by 7:30 we heard the band tuning-up. The opening numbers, classical pieces and marches, lured in the crowds.

"I hope they don't do 'All I Want for Christmas' or 'How Much is that Doggie in the Window,'" I joked, and Eddie and Rolly laughed. Frank loved all music; country, western, opera, do wop, blues, jazz and everything in between. But if either of those songs came on the radio, he changed stations immediately. Once steaming back from the Middle Bank, I saw him launch a judo kick at the radio while "Doggie" was on. The *Stanley* rolled unexpectedly, saving our communications gear, but Frank landed on his back, and hit his head on a spoke of the wheel.

At the 8:30 break a few more musicians joined the band. One of them had the largest saxophone I'd ever seen, a baritone sax. Gleaming gold, four feet long, it mirrored the lights of the bandstand. They introduced the "Tennessee Waltz" as the "Nantucket Waltz," then played "Harbor Lights." Frank and Eddie had found spur-of-the-moment dance partners. Eddie was a capable dancer, but Frank was Hollywood smooth. His partner was obviously enjoying herself, even on the cobblestones. Taller than Frank but no one noticed. What the onlookers saw was a graceful pair to be envied.

The band shifted the music on their stands and we heard a totally different sound. Heavy on sax and clarinet, a sultry blues number *I wish I was a catfish swimming in the sea...* At every chorus, both the tempo and the volume went up a notch, hypnotizing in its earthy trance–blue-blooded Brahmans jumping and jiving. Before the end, every house in town and all the boats in the harbor were rocking to the blues. At 10:00 the band finished with "Goodnight Irene" with everybody singing along.

Frank came over, sat next to me, pulled out his silver Zippo lighter, and took a deep drag. "How come you weren't dancing?"

"I'm not very good at it."

"You'll always be bad unless you practice–is your plan to always be bad?"

"There weren't girls my age," I whined.

"All of those old bags, those twenty-year olds, would much rather dance with you than with each other. Besides, nobody knows you over here; nobody will ever see you again. So what if you screw up a little."

I shrugged, but he was on a roll.

"Men who are denied the presence of women start to miss everything about them. Hearing a woman laugh is one of life's greatest joys. Listen carefully; it sends so many signals. A woman's laugh can be the most powerful aphrodisiac. It's important to respect all women, and that includes the dried-up old bitch trying to get you to understand geometry, even if she has forgotten how to laugh."

"Sixteen-year-old girls?" I pressed.

"Of course. All women vibrate with energy, giving off signals. You just have to learn how to read them. Their laughter says come, move closer and take my hand, talk to me so we can laugh together and enjoy each other. Occasionally, it may sound as if they are laughing at you, but they probably aren't. They're probably more nervous than you are. Most women don't like to take the initiative, so it's up to you. And don't try to be so macho. It's okay for a man to read and write poetry, walk down Main Street with a bouquet of flowers, dance and sing, or enjoy an art museum. Just because John Wayne doesn't do it doesn't mean *shineola.* Everybody knows you're capable of doing a man's work. You don't need to arm wrestle a dance partner to prove yourself. She'll know the instant you take her hand in yours. She'll put her other hand in the small of your back and touch your life force. It's impossible for either of you to mask it. She'll know–without a doubt–and so will you."

Impressment In New Bedford

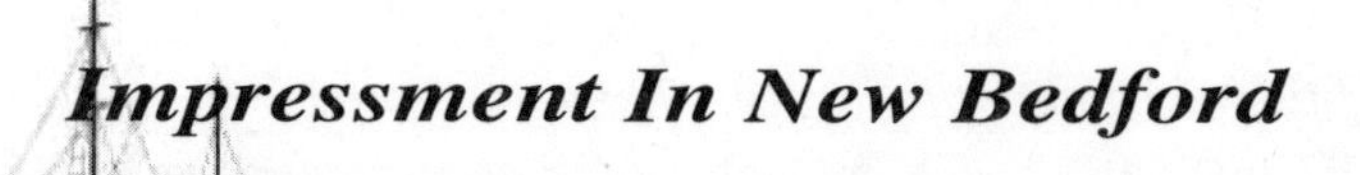

Gie him strong drink until he wink
That's sinking in despair
An' liquor guid to fire his bluid
That's prest wi' grief and care.

Robert Burns, *Solomon's Proverbs, xxx 1. 6,7*

"Who wants to fish Georges?" Frank asked.

"Me!" I said. Normally the time and fuel required for the trip from Plymouth to Georges was prohibitive. However, from our current position in Nantucket, it made sense. Having laid out the bearings the night before, I was hoping he'd suggest it.

"Okay," he said, "It's settled. We're off to one of the richest fishing grounds in the world. Skip, you've never been?"

"No."

"We'll start out across the shipping lanes and the Great South Channel, an ocean river that drains the Gulf of Maine. Then head toward the western part of the bank known as Cultivator Shoals. Georges was discovered in the early 1500s by Giovanni da Verrazano. He named it Armelline Shoals, after an evil papal tax collector back in Italy."

"Why did he name it after someone evil?"

"Because he thought it was an evil, dangerous place. The Cultivator's floor is a series of giant ripples. At the eastern end is Georges Shoal, and in the middle of this is an area that contains soundings of one and a half to four fathoms. A hundred miles from land and water depths of nine to twenty-four feet, less water than inside Plymouth Harbor. Verrazano must have been scared shitless! With the slightest swell you see waves breaking–white water and no land in sight, not from the tallest mast. Old timers used to joke about playing bocce or baseball, depending upon nationality, at low tide. Anyway, about a hundred years later the English renamed it Georges to honor St. George."

After the long steam, Frank paused to concentrate. The tides on the bank were powerful and unpredictable, and required steady vigilance. "Ragged bottom in parts of the Cultivator where the sand changes to rock can rip our net to shreds," he said. Stepping outside to balance on the towing cables feeling the doors moving over this unfamiliar bottom, he was, like all good skippers, attuned to the subtle vibrations sent up to the boat from the gear moving across the ocean bed. "What do you think, Eddie?"

Eddie, already in the wheelhouse, looked at the fathometer. "*Sweet Jesus*!" Immediately he flipped off the steering ropes and turned us into a maximum right turn.

Without needing an explanation, Frank shouted, "Get the gear up! Get it *up*!"

That's when I realized Eddie must have seen something massive in our path. Rolly slammed the winch into gear, starting both drums, and the towing wires snapped, telegraphing their heavy net signal. Moving fast, we got our gear safely on deck, along with a mountain of fish.

"God awful Rocky fucking Mountains down there," Eddie said. "Like towing a net over New York City. Could be some big stones in the bag, but I don't think it's sharks again."

"I bet a thousand nets have been lost down there!" Frank shook his head, impressed. "Eddie, you are a genius, an absolute erudite Einstein. Your instincts saved us hours of labor and probably our net."

"Aw, shucks, Cap't," Eddie feigned modesty, and grinned. "T'warn't nuthin."

"We can set up a coupla buoys to guide us after dark," he said.

I knew when he said, "We can," he meant "Skip can" so I got them ready, not bothered by the implication that we'd be fishing all night. When you're on the fish, you stay with the fish. And of course the long hours were not without compensation; our incomes were directly tied to his. But working with Frank was never a tedious chore to be endured. He respected our ability and recognized that our passion matched his. We never felt as though we worked *for* him. He made us feel as if we worked *with* him. Big difference.

We caught lemon sole; the largest and highest-priced flounder, mixed with a few other ground fish. Flounders are graded by size–small, medium, large and extra large. Large and extra large are occasionally known as door mats or barn doors, not to be confused with barn door skates.

"Look," Frank said, pointing. "Scallopers."

"How do you know?"

"Scalloping boats have two large booms secured to the main mast and each boat drags two dredges; one on each side. See?"

I nodded. By "dredge" I knew he meant the metal frame, eight to twelve feet across the opening, followed by iron links joined together in the same configuration as meshes in a net. As I watched, both dredges were lowered and raised broadside at the same time–a precarious operation.

"The trick is to avoid becoming the meat in a dredge sandwich," he added. "Know anything about scallops?"

"That their eyes are similar to ours, with a lens, retina and optic nerve. And that they're champion swimmers."

"Right. See how much longer that boat is?"

"About twice as long as ours?"

"Almost. Could be the *Mary D'Eon* or the *Priscilla*. Scallopers spend five or ten days off shore and carry ten to twelve crewmen. After scallops are removed from the shells, they're washed in clean seawater, placed in white cheesecloth bags and packed with ice in the fish hold. Processed scallops can stay fresh for a long time, increasing the odds that a scalloper will have a successful trip. Even so, there are horror stories of boats running out of fuel and being towed to port. Last year the *Wild Duck* was forced into Halifax, and the crew had to scrounge bus money back to New Bedford." He checked his pocket for cigarettes and pulled out an empty pack. "Shit, be right back."

Rolly waited until Frank disappeared into the fo'castle and said quietly, "Last year we ran out of fuel on the backside of the Cape. We borrowed a five-gallon can from another boat. They offered to give us more but Frank said we could make it easy. We ran out again at Woods End and brought the *Stanley* into Provincetown using the kicker engine. We could have borrowed more from another passing boat, but running out twice in one day was too humiliating for Frank."

I just had time to nod before Frank returned. He distributed cigarettes, passed his lighter around, and for a moment all of us just stood and smoked, enjoying the fresh sea air and the kick of nicotine.

"Working on a scalloper is about the same as steaking whiting," Eddie said. "Same level of monotony, just lots more of it. The biggest difference is the knife is smaller and not nearly as sharp. People usually don't slice off a finger with one of those. It's one of the few things that works in favor of the fisherman. But as a rule, scallopers cut in much rougher weather than we do, and on the dog watch it's easy to slip and make a mistake."

He dug around in the lazarette and found the blank for a scallop knife. It looked similar to a stainless steel dinner knife except for the narrower blade and a graceful S curve. He wrapped black cloth electrical tape around the handle and passed it to me. "It's gotta fit in your palm, it's gotta fit just right. Keep wrapping until it feels good; maybe a little more on the butt end."

It took the whole roll but Eddie was right. I knew when it was finished, it felt perfectly balanced.

"A custom-fitted handle," Eddie said approvingly. His knife handle had white edges on the seams of the tape where the salt water had bleached them. Salty, well used and well cared for; a work of art.

"How fast are the good guys?" I asked.

"Same as whiting–keep a shell in the air at all times. There's a contest every year to see who can shuck the fastest. It's a hard-fought battle, like the Olympics. Guys from all over Canada and the east coast show up, but it's usually won by someone from New Bedford, or maybe Gloucester. It's hell to pay when a guy from Nova Scotia wins. It hurts to admit it, but some of those Canucks are pretty good, too good on some days."

"I hope they never get the idea that we could fillet flounders out here!"

"I'm sure somebody has thought of it, but I'm damn glad the idea didn't stick." Eddie picked up a scallop. "Tuck the corner of the shell against your stomach. Insert the knife so you scrape the inside of the shell, and cut the muscle holding the two shells together. Cutting as close to the shell as possible gives you the most meat."

As I worked, he lectured me on the two types of scallop: deep sea scallops, with shells measuring five to eight inches; and bay scallops, which rarely grow larger than three inches.

"Bay scallops are the ones that wash ashore on the beaches of sheltered coves on Cape Cod. When you see people walking along the beach right after the storm, they're looking for bays."

Frank hitched his trousers down a notch, and marveled at the way Eddie flicked the scallop meat into the large kitchen bowl. But when the beautiful shell and three quarters of the scallop went overboard, he said, "Whatta damn waste."

"I agree," Eddie said, "but their use is limited. They've tried grounding up the shells for chicken feed, but it cost too much to unload, clean, grind and ship them. Using the guts for cat food never caught on either."

"Can we use it for lobster bait?"

"Nah, too soft and slimy and it wouldn't last long enough."

"How about using it dried for goldfish food, or maybe plant food?"

"Don't know, Capt, probably take some scientist type to figure it out. As far as I'm concerned, only one way to go." Eddie gestured at the now-full bowl. "Get Troy to deep fry 'em."

Frank turned to me. "Get ready for the perfect scallop dinner. Fresh out of the water, with Troy's homemade tartar sauce, roasted potatoes, a fresh summer garden salad."

My stomach grumbled with sudden hunger and I tried to shuck fast, like Eddie.

"Occasionally, restaurants, especially seedy inland dives, try to pass off skate wings as scallops. You gotta listen to how they pronounce it. ScALops instead of scOLops. In wings, the meat is horizontal; in scallops, it's vertical. Sometimes they cut skate wings into nice little circles, but that's a real insult to a deep sea scallops. I've been to places where they tried to pass off the muscles of sea clams. Sea clams are better than skate wings, but they're coarser grained and much tougher."

"Gee, Capt.," teased Eddie. "You really should pay more attention to your food."

"Ha ha. Culinary snob. I don't deny it."

The dinner Troy prepared that evening was outstanding, just as Frank promised. Pushing myself away from the table was no easy task; but every scallop had been eagerly consumed and there was no excuse not to go back to work. Our catches increased that night after ten o'clock and we hauled in very little trash. The southwest chop running against the tide drenched us for the last three tows, which meant we were in full oilskins. Our deck lights blazed like an old lady's birthday cake.

At midnight I was eager for my break. Stripping off my foul weather gear, sudden movement in the water caught my eye. It couldn't be... could it? It was! Scallops! Thousands of them, swimming on both sides of our boat! "Hey, Eddie, come take a look at this!"

Eddie came over, and let loose a whistle. "I'll be damned!"

Rolly was napping and Troy was cleaning up after the meal, but from his position in the wheel house, Frank saw us peering into the water and came hurrying out.

"What the... holy shit, that's a lotta scallops!"

"I've never seen anything like it!"

"Me either!"

"*Never?*" I asked, surprised. I was almost as amazed by that as by the sight of all those scallops. They shook their heads, and we watched in silence for several minutes. *A remarkable sight,* I'd tell my children and grandchildren whenever they begged me for stories about my adventures at sea. *I've never met a soul since that saw that many scallops!*

Finally Frank explained, "They give a strong squirt and lift themselves up enough so they can float in the tide. Another puff and they go a few inches higher. It's all dependent on an upwelling current."

"There sure as hell is enough current here," Eddie said. "I bet we could just dump the net over and hold it against the tide and it would be two-blocked with fish."

Without meaning to, I spoke my thoughts: "How far can they swim? How fast? Why do they swim? To find a better location, to breed? Why are their eyes in the front if they swim backwards? Are they on the move all year or just at certain times? Is it an advantage to have one large adductor muscle like the scallop or two smaller ones like the quahog? Is their ability to swim an evolutionary advantage? Is that why they don't have a foot?"

"Bang bang bang!" Eddie clutched his chest as if he'd been shot by my rapid-fire questions.

But Frank grinned. "Like I always say, sometimes knowledge is knowing what you don't know!"

Not nearly as dramatic as swimming scallops, our other visitor was a layer of dead man's fingers; sponges with large finger-like lobes. Oyster-colored, waterlogged dinosaurs from the deep; hardly changed even after six million years of existence. I marveled for a moment, then shoveled them back into the water.

It had been a brief, productive trip and we used the long steam into New Bedford to catch up on our sleep. When we docked, I was surprised to see no kids. Usually in the summertime they were everywhere–playing with old dories, spare nets, bumper tires, rusty balls from the head rope, anything they could find. But the dock was deserted.

We unloaded, cleaned up and ate supper. Troy bought loaves of

Portuguese chicken bread, salami, native tomatoes, basil, and three bottles of Chianti. He'd bought enough in case company showed up, and sure enough, Whitey from the *Gannet* showed up with a case of beer and a jar of pickled eggs.

"Hail, mighty captain," Frank greeted him. "It is the hour for drunkenness! Drink without stopping! Drink wine, drink poetry, drink virtue; drink as you wish."

Whitey raised his cup over his head and announced:

O Captain! My Captain! Our fearful trip is done,
My ship has weathered every rack, ten thousand codfish we have won,
New Bedford's near, the bells I hear, the buyers all exulting.

Frank loved hearing Walt Whitman paraphrased, especially by a friend, and applauded, Cigarillo in hand. They fell into discussion that went from fish prices, to women, to Eddie's recent predicament, to the weather and back to the price of fish.

Shouts alerted us to more company, and we were joined by the crew of the *Carolyn M*; intelligent, hard-working entrepreneurs. What they lacked in formal education, they made up for in a no bullshit love of freedom and driving ambition.

"We're all capitalists," Frank declared, "working for our money and trying to put the capital to work in another boat, a rental property or anything to keep the pile growing."

"Amen," said Whitey.

"Comrades!" shouted Frank as another crew walked by, "Greetings in the name of the Communist Party! Come and share our wealth!"

I looked around quickly, nervously, waiting for someone to get pissed. Everyone knew Communism was an evil force that threatened to ruin our country! But everybody howled and celebrated capitalism with a free beer.

Of course nothing got past Frank; he saw my apprehension turn to relief and confusion, and turned his full, wound-up attention to me. "Skip, think of a class in math. I get 100 on my test and you get a 60. On the first day the teacher takes 10 of my points and gives them to you. This is fair because I don't need 100; a 90 gives me a good grade and allows you to pass. But on the second test, I don't try quite as hard because I know the teacher will skim a few points from me. You don't try as hard because you know the teacher will give a few points to you. By the end of five tests both of us are getting lower grades because incentive has been removed from both the top and the bottom. The same is true of farmers, manufacturers, fishermen, and sales people and so the whole system loses incentive. The value of excellence is corrupted."

Something else I would never learn in school! I enjoyed listening to them complain, brag, joke, talk about women, kids, boats, fish and just about every other topic.

When the first case of beer was gone, we moved to the closest bar, the Green Mooring. Dim and sparse, it smelled stale. The lights appeared brown, fly-specked with several bulbs missing, the floor uneven. The type of place where you could get seriously hurt, seriously drunk, seriously lost. In fact, if you were not serious about your drinking, you would be well advised to leave.

Rolly said to me, "I came here with Frank last year. There were these two big guys, big and dumb like morons. They thought Frank was an easy mark and started to give him a full ration. Frank flattened them both so fast with a head butt that neither one knew what hit him, and there was blood all over the place."

"Wow!"

"Then Frank turns to me and says, *So Rolly, what should we drink tonight*?"

"Ha ha ha! Yeah, that sounds like Frank."

"Well, well, whose little granddaughter is this?" boomed a voice raspy from too many cigarettes and too much cheap booze. I saw an enormous belly and an even bigger ass that hid the bar stool like a total eclipse. Bald head, fading tattoos.

Frank said calmly, "Don't hassle the youngest member of my crew. He's wrung more saltwater out of his socks than you'll ever sail on."

"Oh yeah?" Lard Ass started to slide off the stool as if to intimidate Frank with his anger and bulk, but thought better of it as Eddie, Rolly and Troy appeared, obviously with us.

We went up to the bar. "What's on tap?" Frank asked the barmaid, a mean-looking bitch who glared at me through rattler eyes that had forgotten how to smile. Thick wrists, fingernails chewed to the quick, she wore her thinning hair in grubby, pink rollers.

"'Ganset or Pabst."

"No Bud?"

"Pabst. Five," Frank sighed; not that he objected to the brand. He just hated not having more options.

"Could I please have a hamburger?" I asked.

"This is a bar," she snapped, "not some juvenile burger joint."

Eddie nudged me. "Dumber than a douche bag. I hear she'll suck the chrome off a Cadillac, probably doesn't know how to cook a hamburger."

I saw a man in a dark blue suit, white shirt and a tie held at half-mast with a gold clasp. His shoes, once spit-shined, were scuffed and dusty. A battered violin case sat on the bar next to him.

"What's in there, some kind of gun?" Frank asked.

The man's reply was too garbled to understand. Between his Norwegian accent and the alcohol, it came out as a singsong answer, a blur of up and down sounds. After standing near him for a few moments, I was nauseated by the odor of urine.

Another Norwegian interpreted for him. "Jens is scalloping and after every trip he comes in, takes his shower, a sauna and goes to his tailor. Has a custom-made suit waiting for him and he wears these clothes until he comes back in again, eight or ten days later. He throws the old suit away, puts on the new one and so it goes."

"You mean he wears his oil skins over that suit, over his white shirt and tie?"

"Summer and winter."

"What's in the case?"

"He used to be a concert violinist, played all the big halls in Europe but he can't even tune it now."

"What's his problem?"

"Booze."

Rolly tapped my arm and pointed at an old guy making his way through a pitcher. "That's Feathers."

He didn't bother to lower his voice, so neither did I. "Why do you call him Feathers?"

"Balls are small, like a canary's. Light as feathers." He pointed to a couple of rough-looking characters throwing darts. "There's Hawky and Spitty. Steer clear."

"Okay, thanks."

Just then two big guys came in and spotted me. The rest of the patrons moved aside. *Cops in here every night... no place for kids.* I looked for Frank, but he was engaged in conversation, and then my view of him was blocked. Large shoulders, short, massive necks, strong arms;

too focused, too purposeful and much too sober to be here. Definitely not looking for a relaxing brew before heading home! Lard Ass sat beaming. That son of a bitch was enjoying this! Damn his red, greasy eyeballs! Did he call the cops?

"C'mon, let's go," said one. A nod of his head towards the door, his hand on my arm. He was dressed like a fisherman. Plain clothes cop? *Shit shit shit*!

"Go where?" I squeaked.

"We'll talk outside," said the other guy.

"Evenin' Capt," Frank appeared suddenly. "Filling bunks?"

Strong Arm stared at him, reluctantly removed his hand and asked, "You getting a full share, kid?"

I shook my head.

"I'll give you a full share and no dishes to wash. Come on, let's go fishing."

It took me several seconds to realize they weren't cops at all, but fishermen offering me a job. Relief washed over me. "Thanks, Capt, I appreciate the offer, but I'm really happy where I am. Besides, I'd only be with you for a couple of trips, I'll be back in school by September."

"Damn," he muttered. "Savery always gets the good ones."

"The best ones," Frank said.

The skipper shook my hand. "If you're ever looking for a berth son, give me a call. My name is Terry Stevens and I own the *Seven Cs.*"

Frank laughed easily. "That's a lot of territory to handle. Want a beer?"

"I got this round," Terry said, putting enough money on the bar for several more. His mate had found an unwilling deck hand in desperate need of sobering up, and they were off before he changed his mind.

Neither Frank nor Eddie paid any attention to this brief encounter, but I found the vicious cycle of work at sea, then three or four days of unconsciousness ashore troubling. Had I, like most of the others in the bar, been intoxicated, I'd be on my way back to Georges. I'd thought that impressment–gangs forcing men to join their crew–had only happened in the hey days of sailing. What did the victims think once their stupor ended and they found themselves headed for places unknown? And what about the families they left behind? How did they find out? Did word spread–*Don't expect to see young Billy for a while; he's taking a little ocean cruise*? Whaling ships sailing out of Nantucket or New Bedford never returned with the same crew they started with. Dropping off burned-out men and picking up new ones in ports as diverse as the Azores, Canaries or Hawaii. The man I saw dragged out of the Mooring didn't leave behind weeping loved ones. No prolonged farewells. Not even the barmaid would miss him.

Noticing my expression, Frank said, "Skip, one of the occupational hazards of this fishing business is alcoholism. We create our own heavens and hells right here on earth, every day with our decisions. Alcohol is dangerous. Drugs are worse."

I nodded, felt worse. Heaven and hell, not abstract places anymore; now I knew where to find them! It made so much more sense than all the burning fires and billowy cloud talk. The scene I had just witnessed felt far more frightening than losing a hand; much more like losing a life.

I thought about my father, and wondered what my life would have been like if he'd been a fisherman instead of working for the Electric Light Company. For all practical purposes he followed the same cycle of work and coma, with weekends allowing more time to avoid living, more time to stop thinking and numb to both ugly reality and sublime beauty. Was the pain so overwhelming? Were these conscious decisions, or just many small steps down a descending ladder? I walked back to the *Stanley* with a firm resolve to enjoy, to fully appreciate both the work at sea and the time ashore.

Lightships And Hardships

"Sail on!" it says: "sail on, ye stately ships!
And with your floating bridge the ocean span;
Be mine to guard this light from all eclipse.
Be yours to bring man nearer unto man."

Henry Wadsworth Longfellow, *The Lighthouse*

Frank navigated us out of New Bedford Harbor and past Fort Phoenix, with Wilbur Point on our left. Around ten at night I stepped into the wheelhouse to see if he wanted me to take the first watch.

"Thanks, Skip. Yeah, that'll be good." He tried to hide it, but I knew he was having one of his headaches. "Call Rolly before the Horseshoe, and call me at Rose and Crown."

"You got it."

"Why don't you plot our course down to Nantucket Lightship? I want our time to Woods Hole, East Chop and Great Point."

"Okay." The courses were fairly easy. I did them all once and recalculated them without looking at the first bearings. The times and distances were more complicated. Frank could do them in his head, but I struggled. Painstakingly I did all the figuring on paper–twice–and still didn't dare tell him what I'd come up with. "I'm just so bad at this," I finally said.

"You're only bad because you think you're bad. You resist learning."

"Why would I do that?"

He shrugged. "Habit, probably. Not doing it is a lot easier than learning how to do it."

"But what if I do it wrong?" As if that made not doing it the preferable option.

He looked at me without speaking for such a long time that I was embarrassed, and went back to my figures, aware of how much crossing out and mental swearing I was doing.

"After the Pilgrims sighted Cape Cod, Captain Jones tried to sail the *Mayflower* south to the area belonging to the Virginia Company's charter," he said. "This required plotting a course around the back side of the Cape and through Nantucket Shoals. Half way across the Atlantic, the *Mayflower* fractured a main beam in the middle of her hull. The crew jury-rigged a temporary fix, but imagine what stresses that put on other structures? Imagine what it was like to lie in your bunk while a critical support cracked inches above you?"

I shook my head. Normally conversation would have distracted me, but his voice kept me focused, and I concentrated on the figures while listening to him.

"Nantucket in mid-November, in a sailing ship, with marginal charts, is enough to challenge the strongest of faiths. The roaring breakers in the shallows of Nantucket Shoals must have been more unnerving than anything the Pilgrims encountered in mid ocean." He paused and rolled the pack of Luckies from one hand to another. "During one storm in October of 1841, twenty-five ships were wrecked in this area. The Pilgrims wisely decided to turn around and head back to Cape Cod. After experiencing the backside of the Cape and the shifting sands of Nantucket, Provincetown must have seemed like the haven they were searching for. During the heyday of sailing, P'town sheltered up to a thousand ships at a time from the fall and winter gales of New England."

"I'm finished," I said, and showed him the numbers.

With a glance, he nodded his approval. "Skip, plotting a course is fundamental and you've got to learn to do it with the same confidence you use in Plymouth. Sure, there's a lot at risk: five men, this boat, and your reputation. But there are thousands of skippers all over the world doing this same thing every day. The good ones do it carefully and then check their numbers, the way you just did."

"Can I write the bearings on the chart?" I asked.

"Hell no, confidence and excellence come from practice. Do them once more after Rolly relieves you."

"Okay. Get some sleep. Feel better."

"Okay."

I woke Rolly at 2:00 a.m. and he joined me on deck. Took a second to get his bearings then assumed position at the wheel. I told him I'd keep him company for a while, and in silence we steamed through the peaceful ocean; black but for the million stars reflected on the surface.

As we passed the Nantucket Lightship, I thought, as I always did, what an oddity they were. Vessels that never moved; doomed, not to eternal wandering, but to a never-ending anchorage. Their crews went up and down, but never to a new, exotic port of call.

As if reading my mind, Rolly said, "I'd rather steak whiting any day!"

"Me too." Lightships have two masts, 45 feet from the waterline, and each mast carries a large, bright lantern. They average 125 feet long, 30 feet abeam, and draw 11 feet of water. Usually they're bright red with large white letters identifying the name of the station, in this case, the *Nantucket*. She was twice the size of the *Stanley*, but probably felt half as big if you had to spend a month on board! Especially in the dense Nantucket fog. I'd heard horror stories of crews that spent weeks seeing no farther than their own vessel.

All lightships had massive foghorns capable of penetrating the best of earmuffs. In locations like Nantucket, it was common to hear the horn blasting every other minute for a period of two weeks. Lightship locations were not selected for their placid waters. Invariably, they were in the tide-torn areas of the world where it was impossible to build a ground-based lighthouse. Lightship duty was considered the purgatory of the Coast Guard, providing few activities beyond standing duty, reading, playing cards, listening to the radio and making lightship baskets.

But the sea doesn't neglect any of her players for long, and drama eventually breaks out on every stage during an exceptionally foggy night or at the height of a winter blizzard. The Coast Guardsmen on duty will hear a large freighter sounding her foghorn in the distance. A few minutes later the horn will sound closer, and then closer still. The men on duty will override the automatic horn on their vessel and give one long, uninterrupted blast, until out of the fog looms a wall of towering steel rushing past at fifteen knots. Vastly more powerful than a speeding locomotive, and just about as likely to change course, the ship's pointy bow is capable of cutting a lightship in two. Something the Coast Guard tended to discourage.

Frank woke at 4:00, and by 5:00 we were back fishing in the Nantucket Grounds, cursing jellyfish and hoping for a productive haul. Conditions here changed day to day, but the menu usually included fog; Mother Nature's recipe of warm water from Nantucket to the St.

Lawrence, combined with cool air carried by the Labrador currents. Places like Pollock Rip, Orion Shoals, Rose and Crown or Old South Shoal were shrouded in fog an average of 160 days a year.

At the age of ten–my first summer on the *Louise*–I fell in love with fog. The sensation of liquid air going deep into my lungs, the musky taste; the playful, romantic way it softened every edge, blurring objects together into fuzzy gray indistinction, not to mention the audio tricks it played. But most of all I loved the mysterious magic of fog, its ability to move in waves, to hide or reveal different parts of the picture.

But mystery's sister is danger. Fog can be beautiful and exciting, but errors are costly. Charlie Rose taught me the bearings in and out of Plymouth Harbor until navigation became an automatic response for me, and in my mind's eye I could see every buoy, every compass bearing, every detail necessary to safely navigate the channel–southeast by east two minutes and fifteen seconds to the first red buoy; east by south for a minute to the next red marker, east by north for three. The other charter boat captains acknowledged Charlie's expertise, and on foggy mornings it wasn't unusual to see their fully loaded charter boats waiting to follow us out the channel. It left him with mixed feelings; he enjoyed the notoriety but hated the idea of others hanging on to his shirttail. He warned the other captains that it was dangerous to follow him out, and it was. One of his favorite tactics was to locate a buoy, purposely pass the marker on the wrong side, race the engine to create more noise and wake, and have me sound the fog horn with extra vigor. Boats following us would stray just a few more feet to the shallow side and end up aground. *For their own good*, he 'd growl; *Teach 'em not to depend on me to do their work!*

Sitting on the stern, I attended to my physiological needs, a roll of toilet paper sheltered between my knees. I'd taken special care to clean a spot to perch, avoiding the dreaded jelly tentacles. A disturbing idea kept repeating in my mind–what would happen if I slipped overboard? Nobody would notice until it was too late. No one would hear my cries for help over the sounds of the engine. Could I kick off my boots under my oilskins, how long would it take to shed the yellow, foul weather overalls? While never noted in the obituaries, it was common knowledge that many of the recovered bodies of fishermen had their flies open.

These thoughts evolved into a reverse fantasy of *Captains Courageous*. A poor, humble lad falls off the deck of a fishing trawler because he has been laboring for days without rest. After bobbing around in the ocean, exhaustion is about to claim his young and tender life, even though he is a very good swimmer. With only his unconquerable faith and eternal optimism to cling to, he struggles bravely on. Tide, fog, and attacks by monster jellyfish have thwarted his valiant efforts to remain alive. The wind and seas increase–breathing becomes difficult. A triangular fin circles ever closer. As he takes his final gasp of sweet, pure air he is spotted by a beautiful young maiden and rescued by the crew of an ocean liner headed for France. He is adopted by a childless couple who own a fleet of ocean liners. They hire private tutors, send him to the best schools, and eventually make him commodore of all their ships. The young man, now wealthy in his own right, returns to thank the exquisite young woman who saved his life when...

"Skip, get your pitiful, pimple-covered ass in here! What the hell do you think this is, the boys' room at school?" Frank shouted.

I scrambled to help haul the net up to the top of the boom so we could shake it empty. *Shit!* Down came the rain of jellyfish with their relentless stinging tentacles. We removed our protection from the tentacles; hoods, scarves and jackets - anything to keep the jellies away from our skin; washed off the fish and hosed the deck clean with extra care. However, like playing in a patch of poison ivy, total escape was impossible.

Back in Nantucket Harbor we unloaded. Frank pulled me aside and asked me to figure out the shares. He often asked a crewmember to validate the figures; not because he thought he might have made a mistake, but to convey the message that no one was ever in danger of being screwed. The task usually fell to Rolly, since Eddie, who had quit school in the seventh grade, had math skills no better than my own.

I said, "Okay," and waited for him to walk away before releasing a sigh. Going into the fo-castle, I hunted around until I found a pad and a pencil. Then I took the gross income and subtracted running expenses: food, fuel, and ice. Of that amount, Frank, as owner of the boat, got 40%, which was standard, and the remaining 60% was divided among the crew, including Frank as skipper. Okay, fine. But complicating the process was the fact that I had agreed to work the summer for a half-share. That meant the 60% was divided by four and a half. Sometimes called a broken 40, there were many variations; for example, when the owner is also the skipper, he will take two shares and / or pay the cook for cooking only and not involve him in the deck work. A full share is usually granted when you become competent in mending twine.

I had just finished and was going over the math when they returned. Frank divided the money exactly according to my figures with a poker face that gave no hint whether I was right or wrong.

"Okay?" I asked.

"Yes. Fine."

So by some miracle, my figures were right! We collected our cash and hurried into the village, five men wearing the same fragrance: a hint of fish competing with the strong scent of Old Spice.

The next morning I awoke to the thickest fog I'd ever seen. I could not see the winch standing in the doghouse only fifteen feet away. I did see the old whaling harbor filled with sailing ships. Their ghosts reflecting tall masts, drying sails, the activity of provisioning for the next trip. Even the local boats remained tied to the dock this morning. If the natives were not leaving, it must be a clear signal to us. Weather like this created the ideal conditions for shipwrecks without a storm. An unlucky vessel might wander slightly off course and hit a sandbar near Monomoy, in the Pollock Rip Slue or Rose and Crown shoals. Tides would do the rest.

I went up to the wheelhouse to see if Frank needed anything, and found him smoking, in a chatty mood.

"During the heyday of sail, before 1865, slave ships often ran aground, presenting a dilemma for the Samaritans who rescued them. Return the slaves to their original owners or keep the slaves for themselves?"

"What about just letting them go?" I asked. "That would have been the right thing to do."

"You sure, Skip?"

Well now I wasn't! But I nodded anyway.

"Picture this. You've just been kidnapped from your home in Africa, where temperatures are usually 90 to 100 degrees. Your ship runs aground in New England and someone says, *Go, you're free now!* But what do you do? You're wearing a loin cloth. You've never seen snow or fog or temperatures below freezing. You have no friends, no shelter, no way of making money. In short," he took a long drag, held it, and blew it out leisurely, "you're screwed."

"So what did they do?"

"Well, human ingenuity devises the most inventive alternatives. Slaves could sign on to a globetrotting whaler, maybe end up back in Africa. The Underground Railroad, a secret network that helped fugitive slaves reach free states or Canada, offered help. Occasionally, families in need of another strong set of hands might take them in and cross the bridge of difficulties when they got there." He looked at me. "Kids your age, Skip, thousands of miles away from home." He shook his head. "And you think being in school nine months a year is such a hardship."

I looked away. Too early in the morning to argue. Plus, he was right!

Two Bad Shows

The thought of suicide is a great consolation:
By means of it one gets through many a bad night.

Friedrich Nietzsche, *Beyond Good and Evil*

We left Nantucket in the middle of the night when the fog lifted, working our way toward home. Everyone except me had pressing business to take care of in Plymouth–lawns needed mowing, bills needed paying, Rolly's front steps needed fixing and Frank's wife Dot had called to say that she and all three kids were sick with a summer flu. We'd been away too long.

We made the Gurnet landfall, cruised past Saquish, and approached the Bug Light. Plymouth never looked so bright. After our days in the fog, everything seemed brilliant. One of the men stationed at the Bug recognized the *Stanley* and gave us a toot on his small air horn. I stepped out of the pilothouse and answered back with our horn and a big wave.

"How do you know Sonny Santoro?" Frank asked.

"I met him last winter when I was hauling lobster pots."

"Lobster pots in the winter?"

"Until the harbor freezes over, lobstering slows down then anyway."

"How many?"

"Fifteen."

"At the Bug Light?"

"Uh huh. I row out, haul 'em in, and go visit the guys stationed there. They're always glad to see me–not because of my scintillating conversation," I grinned, "but because any visitor is a welcome distraction. I think that duty at the Bug Light is more boring than life on a lightship."

"Must get pretty cold."

I shrugged. "Nah." *The hell it didn't!* Frequently, there would be only three places on my dory without ice: the handles of each oar and a small horseshoe shape of my buns on the seat. I'd pull up to the iron ladder, thump the metal sides to announce my arrival, and climb up to the outer landing. By then the door would have been opened and the guys would lead me to their galley. I had plenty of lobsters and they always had hot coffee and food. We considered it an even exchange, lobsters for hamburgers. It may have been the setting, coupled with the exercise, but Sonny cooked the best hamburgers–extra onions, garlicky mushrooms, stinky cheese and plenty of ketchup.

Thursday evening after we unloaded and cleaned up, Frank called a brief meeting: "Everyone take the next two days off."

"Two days... *in a row*?" Eddie asked.

Frank nodded. "A rich man's luxury!"

"Wow. Okay. Yeah." We swapped looks. Sounded good!

Friday I slept late, stopped at the library, and drifted down the alley to the Boys' Club on Middle Street. I was working out on a fast punching bag when Bob Gloyd walked in. He worked on the Carlansul, and also had the day off.

"There are some guys hanging around downstairs," he said, "and the mats are open. Want to give them a little show?" Two inches taller, 40 pounds heavier, he was all muscle, with a Charles Atlas kick-sand-in-your-face build. He could easily pick me up with one hand.

"Okay," I said.

We squared off, sizing each other up. Then I rushed in, flipped him over my shoulder, and sent him crashing to the mat. Shock distorted his features. I leaped on his chest, but he lifted me up, rolled over, and pinned me to the mat. Slowly, and with super-human strength, I moved him aside and manipulated him into a ferocious pretzel hold. Escaping my grip through a series of contortions, he delivered a foot stomp to my neck. Reeling in unbearable agony, clutching my crushed trachea, gasping hoarsely for breath, I drew on the last of my inner resources to deliver a classic step-over-toe hold that made him yelp with pain. Recovering with a grunt, He flipped me over his back. Like dancers, I knew when to arch and release for maximum distance, and landed with a loud, impressive, painful sounding *thud*.

I heard gasps: *Oh man, that musta hurt!* The *piece de resistance* was the sound of bones breaking; me cracking my knuckles. I writhed on the mat, whimpering, “Okay, okay! Uncle!” I limped over to the wall wearing a beaten expression, rubbing my throat.

In the audience was Julius Ezeas dressed in overalls and working a large wad of chewing tobacco. The youngest of eight children, he demonstrated that each successive sibling arrived in this world dumber and meaner than the previous one. He was 18, but in my class, having repeated a few grades.

Shucking his coat he said, “Hey Gloyd, wanna try that with me?”

“Sure,” said Bob. He and Julius started to fence. It was immediately obvious that Julius was in way over his head, and after about a minute Bob brought the thing to a close with an expertly applied hammerlock. It happened so suddenly that no one, especially Julius, saw it coming.

“You’re an asshole,” Julius said. With as much dignity as possible, he got to his feet, put his coat back on and clomped out.

“Why didn’t you drag it out a little longer?” I asked.

“It was the smell, the smell. I thought I was going to puke all over him,” Bob said.

We changed back into our street clothes and went up to Jim’s Lunch. Stanley Augustus Burgess Junior, known as “Pat” greeted us. I knew him because he worked on boats, but he and Bob were on the football team. Something I knew nothing about, and secretly envied.

Two days off, plenty of money, and not much to do. No one wanted to go home; Pat’s father, like mine, was a heavy drinker. Bob’s father had died when Bob was just a kid.

“We could go cruising,” Bob said.

“With what? You got a car?” Pat asked.

“No. I was thinking we could just ride around on our bikes. Pick up chicks.” Bob grinned. “Gotta take the training wheels off Skip’s though.”

“I got a bell,” I said. “*Rrrrrring!* Chicks love that!”

We laughed, shoved each other, and acted like it was the worst thing in the world, but it wasn’t. Pat suggested we have something to eat and take in a movie. “*The Third Man* is playing.” He gestured grandly as if reading the billboard: “*Hunted By Men–Sought By Women.*”

Reluctantly, we agreed. Even at the height of tourist season, Plymouth theaters ran way behind the rest of the country. Movie selections lasted for three days during the middle of the week, with a new selection

Friday and Saturday, changed for Sunday and Monday and again for Tuesday, Wednesday and Thursdays. When a movie appeared in black and white, everyone stomped on the floor and booed to demonstrate that this sophisticated audience knew Technicolor was the only acceptable way to view a movie. Plymouthians couldn't expect to see *Father of the Bride* with Spencer Tracy and Elizabeth Taylor, *The Men* with Marlon Brando, or *Winchester 73* with Jimmy Stewart and Shelly Winters for a while. *The Asphalt Jungle*, *Sunset Boulevard* with Gloria Swanson, or *Born Yesterday* required patience.

We managed to sit through *The Third Man*, then Bob headed home in one direction and Pat and I headed in another. A hot summer night and everyone had their windows open. As we approached his house, we heard some garbled cursing. Pat opened the door, and I was horrified to see his father slouched on a wooden chair in the middle of the living room. One end of a long leather belt hung from the ceiling light fixture, while the other end had been buckled around his neck as a noose.

His father looked up, saw us, and cried, too drunk to stand on the chair and finish the act. Pat got him to his feet and helped him to bed. I took down the belt. All I could think was, this could have been my house and my father.

Pat came out of the bedroom. "Two bad shows in one night," he said.

I nodded. "Some nights are like that."

Even less anxious to go home now, I walked the streets for a while. My dad had never actually tried to kill himself, but sometimes his actions made me wonder. Several weeks ago he tried to remove the storm windows. It seemed stupid to me, since it was already July, and they'd just have to go back up in a few months, but I didn't say anything. It was 11:00 in the morning and he could barely stand, let alone tackle the heavy, extra large storm windows that required balance and dexterity.

A few minutes later I walked into the dining room just in time to see him falling out the window. I grabbed his belt and a handful of trousers and dragged him back in, but not before he dropped the window. It smashed and a cloudburst of glass rained down onto the porch below.

"Whadja do that for!" he roared.

My mother rushed into the room and saw me still holding his belt. "What's going on?" she asked.

"I pulled instead of pushed," I replied. Horror creased her face as the implications hit her. Fortunately, my mother separated us, as it became clear that I should leave. I walked away, wondering what would have happened had I not been there. He would've fallen one story onto the porch, thrashing around on broken glass, too drunk to feel the pain, he could have cut an artery and bled to death. We tried to keep my father's alcoholism hidden, although in a town as small as ours, there were no secrets.

Walking around in the quiet night, I felt myself sink into gloom. Why didn't school teach us how to deal with situations like these instead of wasting our time with Latin? The phrases we memorized were as stupid as the teachers who taught them. Or what about Oedipus? He killed his father and married his mother. It seemed a little closer to home, but I wasn't able to connect the dots.

A thought, like a song you can't get out of your mind, irritated me: *What did you do on your summer vacation?* someone would ask when I walked into school in September. Would I say, *I helped my friend put his father to bed, then I took the belt down from the ceiling*?

In that moment, I made up my mind. I definitely was not going back to school.

I drifted into the bowling alley, killed a few minutes watching the last bowlers finish their games, and headed home. It was late now and the Bluebird began to empty out. A familiar old man on his bike left with his faithful German Shepherd beside him. Normally, I thought it a comical sight to see the elderly gentleman slowly weaving on his bicycle back and forth down Water Street, followed by his equally unsteady dog. The dog had lost his right hind leg in an accident, but that was not the only reason for his uneven bearing. He'd also been drinking beer all night and was as inebriated as his master. Many nights I had smiled at this couple negotiating their wobbly route home, but not tonight.

Sea Serpents And Scituate

Hissing, hissing at the sky
Expanding over all the harbor
Steaming upward never to lie
Clinging to air like vines to arbor
Misty vapor, foggy steam
Falling up, a skyward stream
Serpentine swirls, my mystic dream
Coming from the sea.

Madeline Johnson, age 11
Bar Harbor, Maine Coast Learning Expedition
© River of Words

We left Plymouth in the cold black of pre-dawn, under steady drizzle. I hadn't slept much the night before, haunted by the image of Pat's father slouched in the chair: his helpless despair, Pat's shame and my own horror. But the rain had a purifying quality I welcomed, and my nose told me there were warm donuts and fresh coffee in the fo'castle.

"Have a good weekend, Skip?" Frank asked.

"It was okay. You?"

"Yeah–everyone vomiting and running for the bathroom at the same time, the toilet got blocked up so I had to fix it. Should'a stayed on the boat!"

"Sounds wonderful."

"I got a tooth fixed," Rolly said. "It hurt like a mother. Still does. Only now there's 25 dollars less in my bank account."

"And I had to repair a hole in the roof for my future ex-wife who spent the whole time shouting obscenities at me," said Eddie. "Did anyone have fun? Did anyone get laid? Skip? Did you have sex? With anyone besides yourself?"

"Besides myself? No."

We laughed and Frank smacked me on the back. Steaming down the channel, escaping from prison; running free, saying goodbye to shore-bound troubles.

Handing Frank his coffee, I said, "The Gurnet looks frothy this morning. I love to see the foam on all three sides of the beach."

He nodded his thanks, felt the warmth from the mug, and took a cautious sip. "On any given day about three per cent of the earth is covered with those foamy bubbles. It's one of the ways the ocean gets re-oxygenated. You know why the waves curve around an island or headland?"

"Because they slow down when they reach shallow water and bend around as they follow the shoaling of the ocean floor."

"Right. Like a column of marching men. The outside ones move faster than the ones on the inside. The closer to the beach, the closer to ninety degrees. In deep water, the waves may travel parallel to the beach, but as they feel the bottom they turn more and more as they climb the incline up the beach to eventually face the shore directly. There's a whole lot of math that explains this and allows you to predict how and when waves will hug the coastline."

"That's why on an island, waves are always hitting the shore head on, regardless of which side of the island you're on," I said and looked out at the rain falling on the sea. "Did you hear the forecast?"

"Clearing by mid-morning." He pointed to a drop of rain on the window. "See that? That individual bead of water was formed when the earth was very young. Most of the water we're sailing on arose from volcanoes in the form of steam. The overall amount of water on the planet remains as a constant, pretty much unchanged from the beginning." He paused for another sip and to appreciate the view.

I knew he was giving me education disguised as entertainment; knowledge hiding under the mask of coffee conversation. But so what. "Does that take into account evaporation?"

"Yes. It's pretty much balanced by new or juvenile water that's forced up to the surface as the continents slip on top of the molten core of the earth. Besides, most of the surface evaporation comes back to us in the form of rain."

We passed through a brief clearing squall, the powerful Caterpillar pushing us forward against the wind. Frank opened the window and the sweet fresh ocean smell filled the wheelhouse.

"Each drop has had a fantastic voyage, starting out deep in the core of the earth, finding its way to the surface," he said. "Maybe spent a few hundred thousand years as snow locked in a glacier, then traveled around the Antarctic Ocean. Maybe wound up on top of some mountain, helping to erode it. Who knows what life it helped to sustain. Did it act as the medium to grow some of our earliest forms of life? Did a dinosaur drink and then urinate it? Was it a lifesaver in the Sahara and then move to irrigate crops in the Fertile Crescent? How many fish have passed it over their gills, have breathed it the way we breathe air? Was it ever a tear on the face of a beautiful woman? Will it baptize a child someday?"

"Maybe it was last night's dew," I said.

"To quote Byron, *Words are things and a small drop of ink, falling, like dew, upon a thought produces that which makes thousands, perhaps millions, think.*" He stepped outside and swiped his index finger up the pane of glass, then grandly presented the drops to Cape Cod Bay. "There you go, back to the ocean. Come back and visit us again. Maybe next time we'll mix you with a little well-aged Scotch. Whadya think, Skip?"

I nodded. "I'd like that."

"Is it possible that you and I are just like these little drops–individuals while we live, but destined to melt back into a larger whole? Ashes to ashes?"

"Could be."

"It's what I believe. All part of the process."

"I like the concept of perpetual balance between the liquid water and glaciers," I said. "If the water were all locked up in ice, the coast would extend out to the edge of the continental shelf. Every place we fish would be dry land. Instead of looking for cod, we'd be hunting woolly mammoths here. A fisherman once dragged up part of a jaw with several teeth still attached and some scientists identified it as belonging to a mastodon. The Middle Bank would be just another set of hills as we traveled to the edge of Georges."

"Ready to go back to school?"

"Yeah, I'm actually looking forward to it." My answer shocked me. Where the hell did that come from? Had Frank been brainwashing me all summer? Was I really ready to go back to school? Somehow I felt it might be true.

"You've got three, maybe four trips before school starts," Frank said.

"Could I do both, go to school and fish with you during vacations?"

"As long as someone wants to take a few days off, sure, I'd be glad to have you."

I saw the Brigida brothers hauling in the center of their fish trap at the neck of the Gurnet. The traps consisted of long sheets of netting, hung vertically, running at a right angle from the shore, one hundred yards into the bay. They remained fixed in place by tall poles, up to a foot in diameter, hammered into the bottom. These long arms of netting led fish into a spiral labyrinth from which they could not escape. In the center of the maze, the nets were pulled closer until the captured fish could be scooped into the attending trap boat. Fishermen caught a variety of inshore fish that might be traveling up or down the coast–usually, mackerel, sardines, herring, and occasionally, tuna. Sometimes the tuna or large sharks fought their way clear by ripping giant holes in the net, thus requiring a massive amount of repair. For this reason, the trap boats carried a rifle or shotgun on board. It's easier and safer to deal with a dead shark than a live one. If the tuna weighed two hundred pounds or less, the men could gaff it; however, several tuna over three hundred pounds moving in a confined area are fast and dangerous. A well-placed shot, away from the meat, made things a lot easier.

"The trap boats remind me of Simon-Peter, Andrew, James and John in the Bible," I said. "They've got the right size boat, they use nets, and they're a family of fishermen, all working the same business as in the Sea of Galilee."

Frank chuckled, a nonbeliever who knew the Bible better than most churchgoers. "When He rose from the dead, He took only three people with him up the mountain, all fishermen."

Eddie joined us on the deck and peered ahead. "How's things in serpent city? See any yet, Frank?"

"No, don't worry, I'd tell you if I did."

"Any what?" I asked.

Eddie regarded him sternly. "Promise? You'd call me the second you saw one?"

Frank held up thee fingers. "Scout's honor."

"One what!" I demanded.

"Sea serpent."

"What? Where?" My eyes scanned the horizon. "What do you mean?"

"There's old man Pierce's lobster buoys right in front of us."

"So?"

"He saw a sea serpent."

"He did?" I looked from Frank, to Eddie, back at Frank. Were they joking? "When."

"In the '30s. Headed northeast from the High Pine Ledge."

"You believe him?"

Frank nodded. "I've known Ally Pierce for most of my life. No more reliable witness than him, far as I'm concerned."

I still couldn't tell if they were making it up, playing a trick on me. I knew Captain Pierce, a no-nonsense kind of skipper, unlikely to tell a tall story just for the notoriety. He never drank on his boat, although other lobstermen often placed a bottle of wine, beer, or other refreshment in the middle of their trap line. The cool water at the bottom would chill the ingredients to a perfect cellar temperature for a little pick-me-up at lunch. This was not Captain Pierce's style. His hands and face looked seventy-five or eighty, but he moved around his boat like a man of forty. He owned a classic lobster boat, the prettiest boat in the harbor, every dimension and every proportion exactly right. As a young man he'd fished the Grand Banks, Georges Bank, and now, Cape Cod Bay. More trustworthy than most priests or ministers, when he started hauling pots, no one could do it faster or better. With his six or seven decades of experience, it seemed unlikely that he would mistake swirls of fog, flocks of birds, or porpoises swimming in formation for a sea monster.

"I always said I'd believe in sea monsters when they found a dead one on the beach, or showed me a good, clear photograph of one," Eddie declared. "But once I heard Captain Pierce's account, well, that was good enough for me."

I found myself looking, praying for one. We all were. "Maybe what he saw was an oar fish," I said. "I've never seen one, but I've read articles and seen pictures."

"What do they look like?"

"Like a huge snake. Cadmium red dorsal fin. They have long, slender pelvic fins that display growths resembling paddles at the tips, that's where they got their name. They have bright red filaments on top of their head, like the comb of a rooster. They can grow to be over 50 feet long and weigh up to 600 pounds."

"You bet your sweet ass, that's one mother of a snake!" Frank said.

"But are they around here?" Eddie asked.

"They're in warm waters, especially around Bermuda. They live deep, three thousand feet, coming to the surface only when they're sick or injured. On rare occasions, they get caught up by the Gulf Stream and end up out of their usual habitats. A sick one, unwilling or unable to fight the current, might find itself a long way from home when a warm ring of the Gulf Stream spirals off near Cape Cod. I met a scientist on the *Louise*, and he said that only one oar fish is caught every ten years or so and the species can survive with half of its body missing."

"Whoa," said Frank. "I think if I ever looked out and saw a 50-foot, 600-pound, snake-like creature with red filaments all over its head, I would call it a sea serpent and forget everything I'd read about oar fish!"

As we made the Farnham Rock Buoy, Frank asked, "Was there much gambling on the *Louise*?"

"Small poker games in parties where everyone knew each other, especially on the way out and in. Why?"

"I've been wondering if we could take out gambling parties on the *Stanley*. We could modify the hull and sell drinks; run out to the twelve-mile limit, and make an overnight night trip. It would be a lot easier than this fishing game."

I considered it. "My grandfather told me there used to be two hotels on the north side of Spectacle Island. The police raided the place about a hundred years ago and closed everything down. He said he was too young to go there but they still talked about it in the police station."

"I'll bet they had some hot times there: gambling, girls, gin and gangsters, maybe some payola until greed took over, all the perfect ingredients. Hmm, nice string of Gs there. If we had the financing, we could take one of those big battleships or aircraft carriers, put in a lot of chrome and mirrors, and anchor off shore. A real floating crap game."

"I'm not sure we could use the *Stanley* even as the water taxi to a larger vessel. She's too slow; we'd need something sleek and speedy to attract the high rollers. How would you feel about buying an old sailing ship and using that as a gambling boat?"

"It's a good idea, but a big financial risk. We don't know if it will work or not. It's interesting though. We could take it to Florida or the Caribbean for the winter season."

We were approaching one of my favorite areas–the low hills of Scituate. I looked at the four small cliffs and thought of Rebecca and Abigail Bates, the beautiful, courageous daughters of Captain Simeon

Bates, the light keeper at Scituate during the War of 1812. When British ships entered Scituate Harbor and burned ten fishing and coastal vessels, soldiers were needed for combat, and there were no guards around the day Rebecca and Abigail saw British ships draw close. Thinking fast, Becky picked up a fife and Abigail grabbed a drum–both instruments had been left behind by the regular guard–and hurried to an area where they could not be seen from the water. They played "Yankee Doodle" as the British invaders approached. About halfway to shore the British paused and considered their choices. Were they headed straight into the harbor where a militia, already angered by the previous British raids, waited to take revenge? The vigorous playing of the girls inspired the officer in charge of the frigate to signal his troops back to the ship. By the time the landing party had returned to the *La Hogue*, the ship had already raised anchor and started to hoist its sails. Two young girls played poker with the equivalent of a modern battleship, staffed with a contingent of Marines, and won the hand with a well-played bluff. What would it be like to hold Rebecca or Abigail close and walk on the beach in the moonlight?

Besides my love affair with the Bates sisters, I liked Scituate's history of shipwrecks and shipbuilding. Well over one thousand sailing ships were built on the North River that flows out to sea south of Scituate Harbor. This high-tech industry of the era employed hundreds of men. North River ships were built in boat yards located not only in Scituate but also in Marshfield, Norwell, Hanover and Pembroke. The 74-gun *La Hogue* and the frigate Nymph had sailed up the North River in 1812 and 1813, and burned or captured all the ships in the boatyards. The British were intent on destroying as many industries as possible. Waterways served as the major transportation routes. Crippling the marine trades could bring victory. The British did damage the whaling industry and made huge dents in fishing and trading.

One of the most famous of the North River ships was the *Columbia*, (sometimes referred to as the *Columbia Rediviva*) the first ship to carry our flag around the world. She was built in 1773 by James Briggs at Hobart's Landing. Briggs, who fought in the French and Indian War and in 1750 volunteered for the Continental Army, was another of my heroes. He manned a watch station on Third Cliff and drilled with a wooden stick. When asked what he was going to do with an old branch, he replied, *I'm going to knock down the first British Soldier I see and take his gun!* After his tour of duty, he arrived home with a British musket under his arm.

By now Scituate Light had appeared on our beam. The builders of the lighthouse had designed it in a way that often led pilots to confuse it with Boston Light and they ended up on the rocks of North Scituate or Cohasset.

If the North River had produced over a thousand new ships in the nineteenth century, the rocks and ledges of the South Shore have claimed at least that many. Fishermen knew the location of shipwrecks and shared the information with other fishermen. Dragging a net over a wreck means hours of repair, or even the loss of all the gear, including doors, cables and the net, well over a thousand dollars worth of equipment.

As we cruised along the coast, Frank kept the radio tuned to the channel most frequently used by commercial fishermen. We weren't paying attention to background chatter as guys bitched about the price of fish and the cost of fuel. But suddenly we became alert as an old, heavily accented Italian voice started shouting *Mayday!* with a lot of Italian mixed in.

Although he was not on the emergency channel, the Coast Guard had received his call, probably from another fisherman. Everyone else on the air stopped talking. Frank turned up the volume and moved closer to the radio. I couldn't make out much of the conversation.

"Coast Guard is trying to get his location," Frank said.

Thirty seconds of rapid fire Italian followed, then somebody with better English cut in and gave the bearings. The name of the boat was the *Sancta Maria* out of Boston.

Frank grabbed the microphone. "*J. L. Stanley and Sons* here. We're about five miles away and have changed course to meet you–over."

"This is the *J. B. Junior II.* Thank you, *J. L. Stanley*; we are about two miles away and have *Sancta Maria* in sight–over."

"This is the *Three Brothers*. We are two, maybe two and a half miles away and steaming to location–over."

"*J. B. Junior II* here. The crew of the *Sancta Maria* is in the lifeboat–over."

"United States Coast Guard, Boston here; are all the crew members of the *Sancta Maria* accounted for and in the life boat?–over."

"*J. B. Junior II.* Affirmative Coast Guard. Everyone is in the boat and we plan to pick them up shortly–over."

"Coast Guard, Boston to *J. B. Junior II.* What are the sea conditions?–over."

"*J. B. Junior* back to Coast Guard. Seas are one to two feet with light rain–over."

"Coast Guard, Boston. Affirmative. *J. B. Junior II*, please let us know when you have everyone on board your vessel–over."

"This is *J. B. Junior*. Affirmative Coast Guard. I'll call you back in twenty minutes. *J. B. Junior* out."

"Looks like an insurance job to me," Frank said.

"What? Why do you think that?"

"Here's an old boat with an ancient skipper who probably wants to sit home and play with his grandchildren. Tell 'em all about those big storms, narrow escapes and how big the fish were back then. He also made sure a couple of friends were nearby and it's perfect weather for this sort of thing."

"How did he do it, do you know?"

"We'll probably never know for sure. The most common way is to open the seacocks, and just let the water in. The challenge is to make sure the boat is never found. Sometimes on an expensive claim the insurance company will send a diver down to check it out, so you want to make sure it's sunk good and deep. I heard of a guy who waited in the bilges of the engine room to close the valves, but he delayed a few seconds too long. The boat rolled over and sunk before he could get out. Between the disorientation and the suction of the hull going down, he couldn't escape and went down with the boat." Frank pointed to the chart. "Look where they are. Three hundred feet of water, on top of a rock pile we never fish. It's an ideal place. A little early in the year, but not bad. The best time is late October because the weather gets really nasty and makes it hard to send a diver down to check it out until the following spring. On an old boat like this, though, in fifty fathoms, it would cost the insurance company two or three times more than the claim to check it out."

"And people get away with this?'

"All the time. Sometimes a crewmember intentionally brings up a door right through the bottom. If the hull is old and spongy it doesn't take much and it looks like a real accident. There's a guy down south who started out on fishing boats–went through three or four, always in some relative's name. Then, he graduated to yachts and made a bundle of money before they caught up with him." He smiled and shook his head. "Never did go to jail–the evidence wasn't strong enough. Just laid low, quietly spending money all over the Caribbean."

We passed Lawson Tower, a tall wooden-shingle water tank with a set of chimes at the top, considered by the town's people to be the most beautiful water tower in the country. Fishermen used this landmark every day it was visible by watching the structures in front and in back of the spire to locate their position on the ocean. This imperfect form of triangulation was reasonably accurate if a second pair of objects, forming a different angle, could be used as guides.

"You know that was built by Thomas Lawson?" Frank asked.

I nodded. "The Copper King."

"Right. He made a fortune, built that tower, then died a pauper. Know that section of Scituate called Egypt?"

"Yeah."

"Know why it's called Egypt?"

"Something to do with the fact that they've been planting corn there since the 1600's?"

"The name comes from a verse in Genesis. Supposedly after the great famine, every country went to Egypt for corn. One year, after a hard drought in Scituate, that farm was the only one that produced sweet corn."

"Oh! I always wondered. They make corn liquor too."

"Very best home brew on the South Shore," Frank laughed. "Anyway, Thomas Lawson had a huge estate there. He also built one of the unique sailing ships of his era, which he modestly named after himself. The ship had a steel hull, carried 43,000 square feet of canvas on seven masts, in addition to six steam engines. The *Lawson* was not a glamorous round-the-Horn clipper; she hauled coal and lumber up and down the east coast for most of her life. The super tanker of her day. Her only trip across the Atlantic ended in disaster. On Friday the thirteenth, 1907, she was lost on Hell Weather Reef. Only two crew members survived."

"Wow."

"The moral of the story is, not always the strongest wind up on top. Something to keep in mind, young Skip."

"I will. Hey, Frank. Remember that argument you had on the dock with Sal?"

He glanced at me. "What about it?"

"Were you afraid of what might have happened?"

"Not at the time. I knew that if any one was left standing, it would be me. But when Eddie and I walked back to the boat I was shaking. I'm not sure if it was fear, frustration or regret, but it was not courage. It was foolish pride."

"What did you regret, not hammering him?"

"No, I felt ashamed because I lost my temper. I lost control. I reverted to the most primitive method of solving a problem. Okay, so we beat the shit outa each other and then where are we? What did we solve? Did we end up with the correct amount of fish based on the winner?" Frank shook his head as if the thought hurt. "There's no question in my mind I would have won. I'm faster and better trained than he is. There is also no doubt that Sal would have done serious damage. He's simply too good not to have gotten in a few solid licks."

"It was better the way you guys resolved it, going out for a drink afterwards," I agreed. "But why is it that people recognize you as the leader or the person who will undoubtedly win the confrontation? How do people know this?"

He grinned. "Let's pretend that you and Frenchy got into a serious fight. Who would win?" "Me."

"Why? Old Jell-O balls is a foot taller and a hundred pounds heavier. Besides, he's older, maybe more experienced."

"Yeah, but I would still win."

"Right. Because you know that bigger and taller doesn't mean diddlysquat. You know he would be fish food after the first ten seconds. Outside of pulling a gun, the most dangerous thing he could do is fall on you. There's another part of this, and it's almost as important. He knows the same thing. Without a word ever being spoken, he knows. He would do anything in the world to avoid a direct conflict with you." Frank gave a rapid left, right, jab at the air and followed it up with a judo chop to the back of his invisible opponent's neck, then raised his knee with enough force to break their jaw before it hit the ground. "If you can conquer your own fear, you will conquer all fear. Frenchy can't fight his way out of a paper bag, but that's not the point. It's much more valuable to be able to think you're way out, than fight your way out."

I nodded, listening hard.

"Now what you need to do," Frank went on, "is project this feeling you have about Frenchy to everyone else. Bigger, taller, faster, smarter–doesn't make a gnat's ass of difference, look at David and Goliath. David thought he could do it. Sure, he got lucky, that never hurts; he was also good and he knew that, too. Nine-tenths of winning is between your ears." Frank took off his cap, smoothed down his short hair. "There are times when you may have to endure the intolerable–just tell yourself you can last longer than the other guy. You're the only one who controls what you think. Most people don't lose, they simply stop trying to win."

I nodded. Everything he said made sense. He made things sound easy and logical.

He sighed. “That little old lady was beautiful, wasn’t she?”

“Yeah. That was a sight, alright! You think she’s done that before?”

“Dozens of times. Growing up she must have seen stilettos, razors and switchblades all over the place. Not to mention Mussolini and all his fascist imbeciles.”

“It looked like she stepped in between her two sons.”

“Did you see her smile after it was all over? She’s lived long enough to think of everybody as one of her own.”

“Even me?” I asked.

“Especially you. The fish are the least important thing you give her. You always smile and treat her with respect. She doesn’t even have to ask. You see her as she walks past the float, and by the time it takes her to walk to the pier, you’ve got one of our best fish waiting–it’s better than going to a market.”

By now, we were up to the “Lover’s Light” or Minot’s Lighthouse off Cohasset, and Frank started to bear a few points more to the east. Minot’s light signal is one, four, three, or, as it’s always translated, *I love You*. Any ship approaching Boston from the south or east is met with this greeting. I couldn’t look at it without thinking what it must be like to see this message after returning from a yearlong, hard voyage.

“I wonder what the effect would be if we hung up huge, flashing signs over the roads leading to Plymouth saying *I Love You*,” Frank asked.

“Maybe we should build a tower on land so people could see the flashing message twenty miles away.”

“Minot’s is considered one of the most dangerous beacons in America. In nine years, from 1832 to 1841, over forty shipwrecks happened there.”

I knew the story, but I liked hearing him tell it. The weather cleared and the brilliant sun reflected off the granite tower and the curling surf around its base. For the first time that summer, I thought about my classmates and how many of them were doing the same boring routine ashore, while I looked at Minot’s from the ocean side. I looked ashore from approximately the same position as Samuel de Champlain, the French explorer, when he first saw the area in the summer of 1605. His Indian guides were reported to have left offerings to the gods at strategic spots along the way. Minot’s Ledge would certainly have been one of the places I’d place my gift to the creator.

Dumping Grounds

When the pin is pulled, Mr. Grenade is not your friend.

U. S. Marine Corps

When Frank announced that our next trip was to a region called Dump Number One, I gave him a glance to see if he was kidding. He wasn't. "But fishing is prohibited there," I said.

"Yes, young Skip. Strictly forbidden."

"So then why..."

"To preserve the environment. The fish are endangered from overpopulation."

I laughed and he grinned. "Okay," I said, "how does *that* work?"

"Too many fish, not enough food to go around. See? We'll be doing them a favor, Poor little things'll starve unless we help out."

Just outside of Boston, this spot where city, state and federal governments disposed of things they didn't know what else to do with, carried heavy fines for anyone caught fishing. But Frank's rebellion was infectious, and excitement grew as we stalled for time, fishing east of Boston until well after dark. At last we headed toward the dumping grounds. Forbidden fruit. Any fish caught here would be far sweeter than those caught elsewhere. We were the Merry Men of Sherwood Forest, about to enter a kingdom ruled by charlatans and impostors. Here to take what was rightfully ours, and screw the sheriff and all his men! On a mission to reclaim our natural inheritance from the corrupt, highborn lords of the land!

"You're sure this is okay?" I asked, growing apprehensive as we drew closer.

Frank nodded. "The legislators who declared the area off limits have never caught a single fish. They have no idea what constitutes good fishing grounds. They're like absentee landlords who dictate what goes on without ever knowing anything about what's best for their tenants."

Technically not an answer. But our Robin Hood had put a lot of thought into this venture with a carefully plotted course that would take us through the most productive area: the middle of the dump.

"Don't get me wrong, it's incredibly dangerous, what we're doing," he warned. "We'll make our first set in total darkness, close to the center of the main shipping channel for Boston Harbor. Without our running lights on, it'll be almost impossible for other ships to see us. And with the net down, we won't be able to make sudden changes in any direction." He gauged our reaction, then nodded. "Eddie and I will be lookouts for the first watch."

"Okay."

The rest of us went below for a quick mug up and a catnap. Despite my nerves, I fell asleep slumped over the table. It seemed like only a minute passed before Eddie called us back on deck. Troy and Rolly climbed off their bunks and we hurried up.

Our eyes accommodated quickly to the dim, silent night, as we hauled in the net.

"I saw some lobster pot buoys in our path," Eddie said. "Wonder how many we caught?"

"Might give us an idea of how productive the night is going to be," Frank said.

We found several pots in the mouth of the net, along with an average amount of fish–nothing extraordinary for the length of time the net had been down. Removing pots from a net is never easy. Usually, the pots break, and pieces get caught in the twine and tear it. Eddie smashed the pots into small kindling and we left the remains hanging in the net to deal with later.

With the net back down, we started sorting and gutting. Right away, something didn't look or feel right.

"Frank," I said, "what's wrong with these fish? They're deformed." I held one up, then another and another, and despite the lack of light we could see they had short noses, incomplete tails and misshapen fins. "This is like Halloween, sort of creepy."

Frank sighed, scratched his head. "More lobsters in this one haul than we've caught all summer," he said, which I took to mean, *Let's wait and see what else turns up.*

Our next set went smoothly, and we hauled back forty-five minutes later.

"This is insane," Eddie declared. "Same amount of fish as anywhere. We could have caught just as many fish in a dozen different places, and leave the lights on!"

"What do you think, Frank?" Rolly asked.

"Well, let's do one more tow, and then decide."

The net went down, and an hour later, we pulled it back and knew from the lack of tension on the wire cables that we had the smallest catch of the night.

"Least we got plenty of lobster," Frank said. "Turn on the lights, we're getting outta here."

I admired the catch. Lobsters of every size, and not many culls–lobsters with one claw. Enough to pay for the trip. Lobsters weighing a pound or less are called chickens; selects are one and a half to two and a half pounds; while jumbos are over two and a half pounds. Many people don't buy large lobsters because they are hard to cook, and also because of the incorrect belief that they are tougher than small lobsters. Troy selected several culls and went down to the fo'castle to prepare them.

I noticed that in addition to the sinister deformed cod, many of the flounders had round, uneven sores with an angry reddish color. "Frank, I just don't like this," I said. "It looks like cancer."

" Okay Doc, just keep the ones that look good."

So while Eddie and Rolly pulled off remnants of broken pots from the net and mended tears, I shoveled the unhealthy-looking fish, along with an unusually high mound of crab shells, off the deck. We were weary and a bit let down; where were the millions of fish?

A strange-looking object that didn't roll quite like a rock caught my eye. I blinked, my tired eyes trying to focus in the dim light. I was about to bend over to inspect it closer when my instincts came into play and jerked me back a full step. *Holy shit!* "FRANK!" I roared.

He came to full alert. "What's the matter, Skip?"

All I could do was point, my hand trembling.

He took one look and shouted "Oh, my God! Everybody, get up in the bow and lie down flat. We've got a bunch of hand grenades on deck!"

We did as we were told. Grabbing the shovel, Frank carefully pushed the grenades overboard through the open scupper–one, two, three. We waited in terrified silence for an explosion, and then Frank gave the signal to move out. No one spoke as we steamed out to the Middle Bank.

Finally Frank said, "Every one of them had the pin in, but I'll bet some of them had corroded down to paper thin. We were really lucky."

Lucky. Everyone nodded in silent affirmation. Mighty Neptune had not made us pay for our transgressions. The wardens of the ocean had caught us red-handed but not turned us in, they did not blow their whistles. Instead they turned their heads and looked away.

"Anyway," his voice regained its old cheerful vigor, "that's not the strangest thing a dragger has ever pulled up, huh, guys?" He lit a cigarette, took a long drag. "Guns, airplane parts, torpedoes, depth charges, roulette wheels, small stills, monkey wrenches, false teeth, whale bones, cameras, bibles, bottles of old wine and new whiskey. Skip, know what we pulled up last year?"

"What?"

"An anchor! Stopped us dead in the water. Heavy as a mother!"

"We figured we'd just throw it back, but no," said Eddie. "Frank had other plans."

"I didn't want to leave it there. Tear up someone's net?"

"The real reason," Eddie grinned, "Frank thought he could sell it."

"Sell an old anchor?"

"I knew it had historical value, but nobody else knew it." Frank said. "A beautiful antique kedge anchor, with a wooden stock at right angles to the flukes in classic anchor design. Probably worth a thousand bucks, right? Well she banged and thumped and smashed against the hull with every roll of the boat."

Rolly took up the story. "Finally we get back to shore. Because of the size of this old piece of junk, we needed both the *Stanley*'s winch and the smaller donkey engine on the pier to lift it onto the dock. And there it sits for months."

"Finally I tried to donate it to the Historical Society of Plymouth. They wanted nothing to do with it."

"So what happened to it?"

"It's rusting behind the Reliable fish shacks along with a small mountain of other shit someone dragged up."

"Well," I said, "last winter some skipper found a dead body. There were handcuffs on his wrists and his ankles were shackled to the manifold of a truck."

"I heard about that," Eddie said. "He put the body in the fish hold, iced it down, and finished his trip. When he got back to Boston, he turned the body over to the police..."

"Who said they had to confiscate the whole catch," Frank put in. "Contaminated by the body."

Rolly said, "I heard about an inshore dragger working off Point Judith, picked up a leather motorcycle boot with the leg still inside!"

We laughed, and then we laughed some more. Not because it was funny, but because normal conversation felt good, and we were all young and alive and pretty soon we'd be eating fresh lobster.

Back at the magical, physically magnetic Stellwagen Bank, the Middle Bank, we set the net; late August in the Garden of Eden. I climbed up to the top of the mast and saw a large Loggerhead turtle gliding just below the surface. Unconcerned by our presence, it was about two feet long, maybe a bit smaller but magnified by the water, and probably weighed two hundred pounds. The sun reflected different facets of its plated back through the clear water, an array of colors from reddish brown to yellow-green. Its huge head and innate scowl gave it the look of an old man slowly crossing the street in front of a Boston taxi.

On our other side, tuna were chasing bluefish. A quarter-mile oval of white water, beaten to lather by the activity of the chasers and the chased. The tuna, three hundred pounds of muscle, were hurtling out of the water in hot pursuit of the blues. The power, the dominance of the tuna appeared magnificent. Sun, spray and scales; everything glistening in the early morning.

A raft of Wilson's petrels flittered over the water following our wake. Also known as "storm petrels" by sailors who believed that their presence forecasted rain, Provincetowners called them "Jesus Birds" because of the way their feet touched the water as they tip toe over the surface. "Mother Cary's Chickens" was another name. About the size of swallows, these birds were dedicated, follow-the-sun tourists, spending their northern summers up here in vacation land and their southern summers on the islands off the southern tip of South America. One of the pleasures of seeing petrels was the fact that they are rarely observed from land in New England.

"Chow!" I heard Eddie shout.

Descending with speed, I joined the others in the fo'castle. Such a divine aroma greeted me! Lobster omelets that were one-quarter egg and three quarters lobster, a smidgen of garlic, gobs of rich butter and the special perfume of fresh, strong coffee à la eggshells. Eddie served me three to everyone else's two, and even though I told myself to go slow and savor every morsel, the meal vanished. I could have eaten at least two more, but rather than be piggish, I topped it off with four pieces of toast and half a jar of jam, then ran back up to the deck.

Frank and Rolly were waiting. Frank pointed at his watch. "You guys are looking good this morning," he said, "lets see how fast you can haul the net in and have it back in the water."

Lots of people hated being timed as they worked; it was seen as an indictment: *Ah just, as I thought! You're not working fast enough!* I knew factory workers complained bitterly about "little people with big watches" timing their every move, striving to improve their productivity. On shore these production experts were viewed as enemies of the workers, people paid to squeeze the last ounce of juice from a person's energy–if you did ten yesterday, management wanted eleven today. With their clipboards and stopwatches they analyzed every move an employee made and looked for ways to improve the task. I never understood why these company people were so despised. If they reduced the lifting, brought a part closer, made a bench easier to reach, or increased the lighting, were these bad things?

Frank simply tried to make us more efficient; part of his lifelong plan for constant improvement, his never-ending battle against mediocrity. The longer the net was off the bottom the less money we all made. Besides, he was an active part of the process. He always left the pilothouse to help us retrieve the mouth of the net, and it was his responsibility to reposition the boat in preparation for re-setting the net.

"Seven minutes," he announced. "Not bad, but not a record setter."

The fact that he didn't bitch about our slower times made us want to please him by speeding up. Truly great leadership skills involved instilling your crew with the desire to perform and search for a personal best.

He never timed us on rough days. When the weather was building, minutes weren't the issue. *There's a good sea running, watch the bag as it comes across*, he'd say, or *Okay, Old Dogs, be careful of your fingers.*

This tow yielded nine barrels of whiting along with half a barrel of butterfish, a barrel of hake, a box of large flounder, a box of market cod and a box of haddock. There were also three large wolf fish and five blue hake. Normally we would have thrown over the bushel and a half of herring, but we were confident we could sell them as lobster bait.

We needed five more tows like this, but six would be better. Then we had to be in Plymouth before 6:00 to unload the lobsters while they were still alive. If they were dead, so were we. There is no market for dead lobsters.

Frank kept a decent average all day with a noticeable increase after noon. On the last tow he could not resist the gamble. There was a large rock pile at the north end of this tow that Frank had been avoiding all morning. By the middle of the afternoon the urge became stronger and stronger, as he inched closer to it with every set. Our last tow was cut short by hanging up after forty minutes. We hauled back to see the right wing and part of the belly in shreds. No one complained, though, because it took a split and a heist to get the remaining fish on deck. Our last set had been almost double the average for the day.

I scolded myself for goofing off but I couldn't help it. The desire became irresistible. I ran up to the top of the mast at full speed and reminded myself–just two minutes, two minutes only, one quick look and back to work.

A Humpback whale surfaced just off our bow. Straight up, it revealed a third of its body in a shower of sand eels. Typical humpie, showing off; an acrobat working the crowd. Capable of consuming a ton of food per day, they scoop up thousands of sand eels in one mouthful with jaws that resemble front loading bulldozers. Their ingenious method of capture using a sophisticated fishing technique is called a bubble net: swimming in a circle, whales puff air and create bubbles. As the bubbles rise to the surface they form a barrier that sand eels won't cross; trapped inside they become smorgasbord for the whales.

"Years ago I contacted some scientists at Woods Hole," Frank said, "to discuss the possibility of borrowing that method using compressed air."

"Really? What did they say?"

"That it was interesting to speculate on the potential for commercial fishing, but no one had the funding to carry out a feasibility study. I made a few proposals; I even offered to lease the *Stanley* to the government."

"And?"

"No. No funding, no study, no mater how interesting."

"Oh. Too bad, it would be a fun project, and no cod to gut."

"Next I suggested involving a Mediterranean country to share the costs. Fish are scarce there and seining is a popular method of capture."

"And?"

"No again." He sighed and rubbed his head. "Whales are smart, but humans are smarter. We can do almost anything animals can do, and do it better with tools. Skip, in your lifetime you're going to see a million things that others have seen before you. If you develop the ability to see something unique in the commonplace, you'll be set for life."

We were running late, so Frank called Reliable and they agreed to wait for us and our delivery of fresh, perky lobsters. As we rounded Beach Point I could see the faint lights of a Ferris wheel turning. A carnival had been set up while we were gone and the lights were beginning to show in the lowering daylight. Like a kaleidoscope of changing colors, an enchanting sight from the ocean. The dirt, the grim and honky-tonk parts of the carnival remained hidden in the distance, with only the beauty visible.

In The Canyons

All night long their net they threw
To the stars in the twinkling foam–
Then down from the skies came the wooden shoe,
Bringing the fishermen home.

Eugene Field, *Wynken, Blynken, and Nod*

Our nomadic movement from port to port was unusual. Most boats fished out of one port 95 percent of the time. Even boats fishing out of two locations, like the *Frances Elizabeth*, kept to a routine for the season and then reverted back to their homeports. By now I had been in most of the major fishing harbors of Massachusetts, which held enormous appeal for me. It was only one small step away from being able to say, *Ahh yes, Casablanca, right after the occupation–I remember it well.* I would be humble; modest, unassuming. Rather than lord my worldly travels over the less fortunate, I would wait for those moments of maximum impact and hope that one of my less sophisticated friends would remember to ask me on cue. The right time would be with four or five girls present, preferably potential dates. *The scar on my cheek? Oh, it's nothing, really nothing. Madagascar, I believe–during the mutiny when I was able to save the captain's life. His reward has been indeed generous and, yes, it is true, I'll never have to work again in my life. So come, live with me and be my love...* Frank said it was always good to throw in a little poetry to cover all the bullshit.

A hard slap on the back brought me back to the present. "Ever heard of tile fish?" Frank asked.

"Sure. Some New Bedford guys are making a fortune selling tiles."

"We're gonna give it a try."

"We are?"

"Sure, why not!"

"But they live at 90 fathoms. Are our cables long enough?"

He shrugged, a kid going for broke.

"And they live in the canyons. Do we have enough fuel for the trip?"

"Guess we'll find out! We'll be at Hudson Canyon by noon!"

We let out every inch of wire cable. Nervous energy occupied our next 45 minutes, and when we hauled back our first tow, the net was brimming with beautiful large tile fish! Fat, brilliantly colored, more magnificent even than parrot fish, with vivid marine blue-green on the back fading to yellow, and a pinkish-red and a white belly. The back and sides had small yellow spots and the dorsal fin had larger yellow dots. Blue, pink, with touches of purple at the base of the pectorals and anal fins made them look like individual rainbows. An adipose fin, larger in males, adorned the head like a crown; the type a marquis or prince would wear, reaching as high as the top of the dorsal fin. Spectacular.

"They make haddock, pollack and cod look like the poorest country bumpkins," Frank said in a voice filled with wonder. "I've just never seen so much color."

"Or money," I said, hoping the catch would transform us lowly fishermen into royalty. *Viscount DeBrusk? Of course, my good man. Everyone knows he lives in the big house at the top of the hill overlooking the ocean. Made all his money in tile fish. Sometimes you can see him standing in the window, maroon smoking jacket, silk ascot, his butler standing two paces behind and to his right.*

Our next tow was even better. "Might be a short trip," Frank said. "Tile fish are plentiful now, but they almost went extinct soon after they were discovered in the 1800s. A sudden change in water temperature killed more than a billion."

"Any chance of us catching a giant squid?" I asked.

"Nah, deep as it is, it isn't deep enough for those guys," Eddie said. "Besides, you'd have to find one that was old, stupid, blind and lame. They're too fast and intelligent to get caught in a slow moving net like ours. Giant squid are used to dodging sperm whales traveling five or ten times faster than we are. Usually they're found in water 200 to 500 fathoms. Besides, they may be the smartest, most versatile creatures in the ocean."

I nodded. A few times I'd seen a common squid capture a small mackerel by the neck, then watched them thrash around in a duel to the death. Plus I'd caught plenty from the State Pier in Plymouth using a lead jig covered with up-curved pins. The squid embraced the jig and their arms became impaled. Easy. The hard part was unhooking them and ducking the black ink they squirted, their only defense mechanism. Nothing on earth smells more vile than three-day-old squid juice. But I never caught one without thinking of its 50-foot cousin with eyes the size of my head, three hearts and a gigantic brain. "I've read that they have the largest brain of any invertebrate and have excellent vision," I said. "That their eyes are the largest of any living creature. But I wonder why? That deep, its pitch black. How much can they actually see?"

"Good question," said Frank.

I had lots more. What did they eat? Did they come to shallower depths to feed? If so, why didn't we observe them more often? How did evolution explain a large bird- like beak in a creature living in the deep ocean? What food lived at the depth of the squid? How big did they get? How long did they live? What about ink? Did these giants have the ability to discharge large blobs of black dye to confound their attackers the way smaller squid do? How smart were they compared to a man or a dog? Were they good to eat?

The lack of information was frustrating and a challenge, leading to my fantasy of capturing one. Fishing uncharted, global waters, the deepest canyons, experimenting with different lures and baits. *World record set by an intrepid fifteen year old.*

The night was warm, so I dragged my mattress up on deck and lay watching the stars. The heavens had been trawled by the master dragger and all the clouds were hidden. Our deck lights were off between tows and no light pollution spoiled the inky blackness as I looked for swans, bears, snakes, dogs, warriors and virgins. It became difficult to distinguish the celestial heaven from the watery one that gently lifted me up and down. The sorcerer of the night was working full time. Looking over the side, I saw clouds of plankton, their phosphorescence lighting up as brilliantly as the cosmic ocean. Without separating beaches, the two seas of velvet fused into one. Looking at the sky filled me with the same wonder as looking at the ocean. Eternal, yet evolving minute by minute.

Lying there feeling the past, present and future, it was easy to believe that my fate was tied to the stars. The idea of light entering my eyes after traveling so far made me resolve to give math more effort. It hit me at that moment that the numbers themselves were trivial; it was about the beauty of understanding. Like Wynken, Blyken, and Nod, we all sail forward on a river of crystal light.

Everything changed while I slept. My mystical glittering sky opened up and released cold driving rain with winds rising to 35 knots out of the northeast. We climbed into our heavy gear, called it quits and arrived in New York with less than half a trip.

Frank's expression was sour after we unloaded. "The price of tile fish is lower than a snakes belly. Doesn't that just figure?"

Yesterday's exhilaration was replaced by gloom.

"Should we hang around the city?" Eddie asked.

Frank looked around at everyone's expression. "Nah, we don't have any money. Let's get outa here."

So we steamed towards the Nantucket grounds again, planning to eventually head for Plymouth. I stayed on deck as the rain cleared, and soon it was good to be young and alive again.

Frank joined me and said, "Six or seven years ago I met a guy named Harold Flagg. He was a chief boatswain's mate assigned to the lightship Vineyard, number 73, stationed not too far from here, a few miles off Cuttyhunk Island." He inhaled, coughed and squinted against a headache. "What a lucky son of a bitch. Scheduled to return from leave and go back out to the lightship on Friday. Thursday afternoon, a hurricane struck and the Vineyard Lightship went down during the middle of the night with all hands. In Buzzards Bay, the lightship *Hens and Chickens* dragged its anchors and ended up more than a mile off station.

Harold Flagg spent the next several days looking for the bodies of his shipmates, and then transferred to Monomoy Point Lifesaving Station, a lonely, desolate place. Over the next several years he patrolled the beach looking for German submarines."

"I can't imagine being in these waters under sail," I said. "It's easy to understand why the Pilgrims turned around, no buoys, no lighthouses. It's hard enough for us; what was it like trying to tack against the wind and tide?"

"During the last century, the lightship at Pollock Rip counted over 500 sails passing through this area in 24 hours."

"Wow! Think of doing this at night, in the winter, with no fathometer, and suddenly the fog rolls in."

"That's how men died. During a strong easterly you can see the shoals and false channels running all the way to Nantucket."

I sighed, suddenly thoughtful and not embarrassed in front of him. "I love the names of lightships–*Stone Horse*, *Handkerchief*, *Cross Rip* --

or the shoals, Shovel Full, Rose and Crown, Orion, Old Man Shoal -- any idea who gave them those names, Frank? Or why?"

"No. Good idea for a school project–research the origins of the names. You should suggest that."

I nodded. The project sounded like fun, but raising my hand and announcing in front of a classroom that I would like to do it... didn't. "You believe in Atlantis, Frank?"

"Damn right! Absolutely. Plato describes it in detail in two of his works. If it wasn't important Plato wouldn't have mentioned it a second time. Ever read Plato?"

"Not yet."

"You gotta start. He was very clear about all the details: a large island in the Western Ocean, near the Pillars of Hercules, or to us, the Straights of Gibraltar. Larger than all the Middle East combined and its people conquered everyone in the Mediterranean except the Athenians."

He paused, massaged his temples, took a drag and blew out smoke. "Some scientists think it was the Azores or Canary Islands or even the Americas. It's been hard to find real evidence because scholars think Atlantis was destroyed in a massive volcanic eruption around 1,500 BC. Personally, I think it may have been much older and was gone long before recorded history."

"I like believing it," I said. "I don't even need evidence."

"You should always demand evidence," Frank said. Then his expression softened. "But in the absence of evidence... faith is good."

We enjoyed a pensive silence, watching our fragile wisps of cigarette smoke disappear into the breeze. Frank turned on the radio to hear some news, and then shook his head. "God, what a mess! Korea's not worth a fiddler's fart, and we're engaged in a 'conflict' over it!"

"I'm more worried about Russia," I said.

"Because you've been conditioned. The whole world is afraid of a commie take over! And believe me they'd love to do just that. They've got a pretty good start, what with China and Russia leading the way. You have to give old Harry credit though. The man has enormous cojones-holding back, waiting for the U.N.. Probably more guts than brains, but so what. People have said the same thing about me, and more than once."

"Do you really think it will be a war?"

"No question about it. But can we avoid war with Russia? The problem is that everyone wants to win, and win quickly–that means atomic war. As soon as we get nuclear, we start to endanger every living thing from bacteria to humans. It'll take great restraint not to be the first to use an atomic bomb, but if we don't, Korea will be a long drawn out affair costing money, lives and everything else."

He popped four aspirins and gulped down some Coca Cola. I knew he hated sympathy, so I didn't say anything as he went on.

"War's like fishing: hasn't changed very much since the beginning of time. Beat each other up with sticks and stones. We like to call ourselves civilized, but more people have been slaughtered and maimed in the past hundred years than at any other time. Our real problem is that technology allows us to do it bigger, better, faster and with a lot more finality. The only good thing about nuclear war is it produces losers on both sides. Maybe we'll be smart enough to learn from that."

"With places like China and Czechoslovakia all turning communist, it seems like they're winning," I said.

"Exactly what that asshole McCarthy is worried about. The real trouble is he has Truman's ear. He's got Harry convinced that everybody in the State Department is a pinko. Talk about paranoid–the guy sees spies everywhere. To get a federal job now, you have to take a loyalty oath and promise not to peek into any executive urinals. The man's demented."

"Is there any way to avoid war?"

"I don't know. All the big religious leaders from Jesus, to Mohammed, espouse peace, but they all have trouble demonstrating it beyond their own personal actions or at the national level. The best way is to have a strong third party to step in the middle and demand a cooling off period. Like the little old lady did on the dock. It's important for the third party to be strong and earnestly desire a stop to the conflict. The U.N. could act as a referee in a boxing match, but right now it's too weak to wipe its own ass, let alone advise two egotistical super powers."

"What will happen if we do start an atomic war?"

"We'll lose everything. All the science; all the poetry. Simple beauties like day and night, in one giant mushroom cloud. Probably the only survivors would be deep ocean dwellers, like those giant squids with their big brains. Just think, they'd be the most intelligent creatures on earth."

He bowed his head for a long time, and I knew the pain was getting bad.

Eulogy

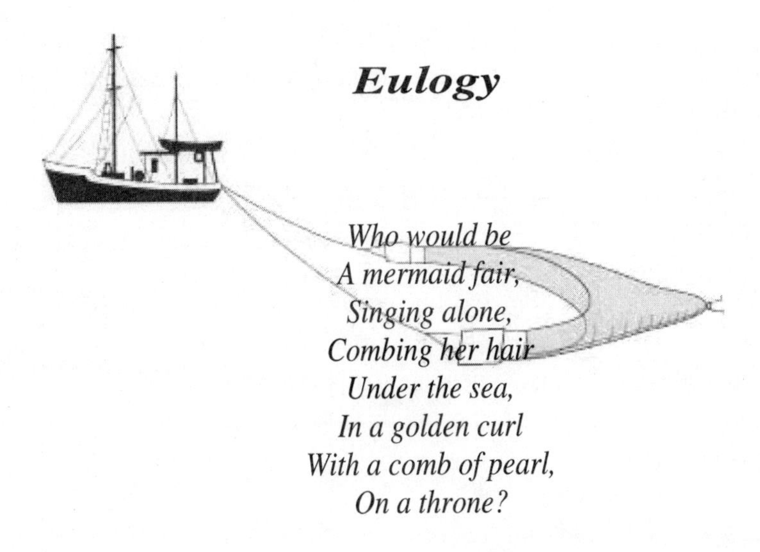

Who would be
A mermaid fair,
Singing alone,
Combing her hair
Under the sea,
In a golden curl
With a comb of pearl,
On a throne?

Alfred Lord Tennyson, *The Mermaid*

Our next two days on the Nantucket Grounds were routine good fishing, with no fog. Frank let me turn in an hour early the second night, but I woke up with a start. The familiar, soothing vibration of the engine driving the propeller changed to a *hump bump hump hump bump* and then silence. We never shut the engine down away from the dock; never. I pulled my boots on with a sense of foreboding and ran up on deck.

"Something's caught in the damn propeller," Rolly said. "Water's leaking in through the stuffing box and the shaft may be bent."

"How bad is it?"

"Bad enough to stop us dead in the water."

Eddie sharpened a knife with enough intensity to prepare for abdominal surgery, and handed it to Frank. Meanwhile, Rolly rigged a heavy piece of chain tied to fifteen feet of rope and pitched it over the side. Frank stripped down to his jockey shorts, and in classic pirate fashion, clenched the knife in his teeth and jumped overboard. One hand on the rope, he disappeared into the water. A stream of bubbles surfaced amid the short, high chop so typical of Nantucket's winds and tides. I pictured him in the icy black water with nothing stable to hang on to. He'd have to ride in perfect unison with the motion of the boat to avoid being struck by the hull, then feel his way to the propeller, locate what was tangled up, and cut it off. All with one hand, since he couldn't let go of the rope. I held my breath, waiting for him to reappear.

In just over a minute his head popped to the surface. "An old lobster pot line made its way past the cage into the propeller and shaft," he gasped, treading water. "Old stray."

"Want some help?" I asked, starting to pull off my sweatshirt.

"No! Can't see. Might start cutting each other."

"Need a new knife?"

"Not yet."

There was a deep abrasion on his right shoulder where barnacles must have ripped his flesh. He forced air in and out of his lungs as he prepared for the next dive, and once again, disappeared.

Another minute passed and Frank rose up again. "Almost got it," he managed to say.

"You sure you don't want help?"

He shook his head, not bothering to squander a precious breath on our questions. One more dive, and he surfaced in less than a minute. "Got it."

"Nice work." We pulled in the rope, then hauled him back into the boat.

He collapsed in utter exhaustion. His breathing was forced, rapid and labored. He had lost his undershorts in the water. Eddie threw a blanket over his shoulders, lit a fresh cigarette and put it to Frank's lips; he took a shaky drag.

Seeing him like that frightened me so much, my heart was probably pounding just as fast as his. "You going to be okay?"

He nodded, then coughed, gagged on seawater and spit. "Just need a minute."

Another anxious sixty seconds passed, then Frank couldn't stand having us all hover, and tried to get to his feet. Eddie promptly slipped a strong arm under him and pulled him up. "Let's get you down to the fo'castle. Put on some warm clothes, maybe take a break. Troy, coffee?"

"Coming right up."

"I'll get the engine going," Rolly said. "We'll be on our way before you know it."

"Okay. Thanks."

Troy and Rolly dispersed as Eddie guided Frank down the ladder. I stayed where I was, in order to nab Eddie as soon as he came back on deck. I didn't have long to wait. "Is he okay?"

"He's fine. " Eddie's relief was clear as he grinned and smacked my back. "Having some of Troy's miracle coffee."

And sure enough in a little while Frank reappeared; dressed, smiling, and breathing normally.

"Lookin' good," I said casually, as if I hadn't just spent the last ten minutes worrying myself into a stomachache.

"Okay let's catch some fish." He looked out at sea, scanned the horizon, found our buoy, casually slipped the big Caterpillar into gear and smiled at Rolly. "Good thing this didn't happen in February. We'd be cooling our asses waiting for the Coast Guard."

"We were lucky," Rolly agreed.

"Three weeks ago I stopped by the Plymouth Marine Railway. Saturday, and the place was buzzing. Most draggers take Saturday off, and that's where they go for repairs. Two Boston boats, the *St. Michael* and the *J. B. Junior II* were in cradles, and John Pinto was waiting with the *Liberty II*. His wheel had been fouled by his own stern line." Frank laughed. "He wasn't happy about it, believe me. So the owner says *When do you plan to pay me?* And John says, *As soon as you fix my boat–can't catch any fish in your yard*."

Eddie and I laughed too. Pinto's temper was legendary.

"One thing I learned a long time ago was the importance of finding the bright side. Look around, stop and think about how much worse something could have been. And believe me, every situation could be worse. There's always one more thing that could have gone wrong and didn't. That's key. That's what keeps a man from being bitter."

We left Nantucket, fished off the Highland for two more days, and unloaded in Plymouth. After one day in Plymouth to settle accounts and re-provision, no August morning looked finer than the one on which we left to fish the North Shore. A friend of Eddie's had called to alert us that Ipswich Bay could not contain all the fish trying to swim there. We landed in Gloucester and unloaded a full boat, mostly codfish, while the radio blasted commercials and southern preachers cried out for salvation and donations.

"Brothers and sisters," Frank shouted, "send ME your checks and money orders, today, yes, do it *now* and feel the cleansing power of the Lord wash your sins aWAY. Put your hands on the radio, yes, yes, *do it now*, dear children, and feel, *feel, the redemptive power*!" He put an arm around me. "Do you wish to be saved, my son?"

I nodded. "Sure."

"Then verily I command thee to take all our soiled garments to the laundromat."

"What? But I don't know how! Besides, that's Rolly's job."

"Rolly has to see to another minor detail, namely, our engine. Come on. Going to the laundromat is fun. It's a mecca for dames."

"Housewives," Eddie clarified. "But a dame is a dame."

Sulking, but not enough that anyone would notice, I stuffed as much laundry as I could into several bags of dubious sanitation, and hiked to the local laundromat. I opened the door to the unfamiliar smells of sweet soap and acrid bleach; the *chungka chungka* of heavy-duty washing machines, out of sync with the efficient *hummmm* of multiple dryers.

She stood there, head down, slowly folding one cup of her small bra into the other. She enjoyed the pace, I thought, it gave her time to think. The tread marks on her face spoke of many miles without all the proper maintenance. Her wrists showed large veins and well-muscled arms. Her clothes all had the same color, a light gray from many washings. She saw me studying the washers, and smiled. "Want some help?" Her voice was low but not hoarse, strong, without demand.

"That'd be great. Thanks."

She opened the first bag and looked in. "What boat you on?"

"The *J. L. Stanley and Sons*."

"Where from?"

"Plymouth."

"How's the fishing?"

"Good, but the price is awful, too many fish being landed."

"Ready to go back to school in a couple of weeks?"

I shrugged.

"Does that mean yes, no, I'm thinking about it, or mind your own dumb business?"

"It means I'm going back to school but wish I wasn't. I'd rather be–"

"On the boat. I know. It's an incurable disease, an awful sickness, that longing to be back at sea." Vengefully, she stuffed four washers with our clothes. Ballerina build, extra long legs, small rear and a perfect swan's neck, contrasted with her arms and hands, which showed overtime hours of hard work. Smiling eyes and feisty expression. "Winter isn't the same as summer out there, you know," she said.

"I know. But school is so boring."

"Got a girlfriend back in Plymouth?"

I shook my head.

"You will this year, wait and see. It'll make school a lot more interesting. I married my childhood sweetheart right after graduation and he joined the Navy–skippered a wooden mine sweeper until 1946, when he bought his own damn boat. Don't be in a hurry to get married, take your time. I know I can't talk you off that stupid boat, but make sure you finish school."

"Want a tonic?" I nodded toward the vending machine. "I'm having one."

"Sure. Coca Cola."

I fished out some change from my pockets and got us each a bottle. As I handed her the Coke, she took a long swallow, and wiped sweat from her forehead with the back of her wrist; a delicate, feminine gesture that I found, to my annoyance, sexy. Was there no woman on the planet I wasn't attracted to? Scowling, I regarded the washer. Always the same message, stay in school. Easy to say when you're a grown up! You forget how stupid it is!

"I'm just saying, fishing is dangerous," she went on. "And I have every right to say it, because I know for a fact. My husband wasn't some amateur. He was one of the best. But he couldn't control the ocean. He died coming home from Georges in the *Sea Ranger* two-blocked with lousy codfish."

"Oh." I lowered my head, sad and sorry for her. "I'm sorry."

"You know, fishermen have the highest fatal accident rate of any kind of workers. Maybe that's part of the glamour. I don't know." She sighed. Her laundry was done. "When your clothes are ready to come out put them into four dryers and turn the setting up to high."

"Okay. Thanks."

Finally she smiled again, and held out her hand. "Good luck. It was very nice to meet you."

"Nice to meet you too."

I watched her walk out, her single basket balanced against her hip.

I headed us in, past the cairn at the tip of Plymouth Beach where the warm land air gusted out to greet us. After three days and nights at sea,

Rosa rugosa, mingled with hot dogs and mustard, carried the aroma of home. Black skimmers fished parallel to the beach. For me, it was impossible not to admire their extraordinary beauty and unique feeding habits. Their tails are forked, similar to a tern's, and the bill is bright orange-red with a black tip, and the mandible is nearly a third longer than the top. Flying inches above the surface, their heads dart down and snap up prey. Today they were feeding on sand eels. Masterfully, their strong, graceful wings, black on top, white on the bottom, and spanning four feet across, missed the water by millimeters on their down stroke.

It was late Sunday afternoon and sailboats were everywhere, gliding over the narrow channel like skaters, striving to run up wind to facilitate the trip back to the yacht club. Sailboats have the right of way over powered vessels, but most of them understood that it took a thirty-ton dragger more time to change direction than a three-hundred-pound sailboat, and granted us first passage. I turned right at the stationary black and white buoy, and headed directly into the unstable land breeze.

Charlie Silva's boat, the *Carlansul*, was right behind us, with Pat Burgess at the wheel. We would arrive at the dock five minutes ahead of them, so they would wait for us to unload. Watching Pat during the last hour, I knew he had his throttle two-blocked, hoping we'd stop at the Gurnet to wash our net so they could dock first. Not a chance! I had hugged the short side of the channel all the way in order to gain the small margin.

One sailboat glided out of the channel just to our left, a second passed our stern. The breeze puffed in unpredictable gusts. A third, crewed by two teenaged girls, moved erratically. I inched us over to the starboard as far as I could. Peg Tavares was speeding down the left side of the channel.

When the girls came too close, passing under our bow, I had no choice but to throttle us down a little. Turning to the left would have meant moving into Peg's course. To my shock, the *Carlansul* was right behind me. Damn! Pat must have cut the corners of the channel even more than I did; must have passed some of the buoys on the wrong side to gain this much.

Frank heard me slow down and climbed up on deck. I pointed to our stern. At that moment, an unexpected gust tipped over the tiny sailboat and the two girls landed in the water, directly in front of us.

I jerked the throttle down, shifted into reverse, spun the wheel hard over, felt it stop, and cranked up the speed again. Frank opened his mouth to object then realized I'd positioned us to offer assistance. I held back a grin. Too narrow in the channel for the *Carlansul* to pass between Peg's speedboat and us.

Everyone appeared on deck now. Frank stepped into the wheelhouse, but didn't take the wheel. "Perfect! This is perfectly perfect," he said. "Look at Slippery Old Silva back there, sitting on his fat arse! Hi ho Silva, away!"

Eddie and Rolly moved to the bow with our life ring, their eyes on the two girls in the water. They didn't appear to be in distress, or in any rush to upright their boat as they ducked, dipped and frolicked. Hair glimmering, laughing mermaids.

"Frank," I said, "I know them. Lucille and Roberta. They go to school with me."

Frank shouted, "Need help?"

"We're fine, thanks," Lucille said. Then she recognized me. "Hey, Skippy! Come on in! The water's great."

"Uh, uh, um," I said. *Brilliant.* The wind had died as suddenly as it had kicked up, and the girls paddled over to their boat and set it right. *Bye bye, Skippy!*

Frank took the wheel and moved us away in order to remain in front of the *Carlansul*. After a minute, he glanced at me. "Smooth talker. I'm impressed. Where'd you learn to woo girls like that?"

"Very funny," I said.

"Hey, Skippy, how about joining us for poker tonight. Know how to play?"

"Not really."

"That's a disgrace. Every man needs to know how to play poker," he said as he eased us in ahead of the other boats. "Let's unload, and while you re-fuel, I'll pick up beer."

"The key to poker is just be the one with the best hand," Frank said, shuffling the well-worn Bicycle cards in a graceful arc. "The highest possible hand is a five-card flush, which means all five cards are the same suit and in sequence. A royal flush, ace, king, queen, jack, and ten, beats every other hand. Next best, four of a kind. Then a full house, that is, three of one card and two of another. Then three of a kind, then two pair, then a pair. Got it?"

"Sure." I sipped my beer and nodded.

"If you hold two pairs and draw one card, for a full house, the odds are 11 to 1 you won't get it."

"Okay."

"If you hold three of a kind and draw one card, your chances of matching the card in your hand for a full house are 15 to 1 and 46 to 1 against all four."

"It'll probably make more sense if we just play," I said.

"Good idea. Okay! Deuces wild, jacks or better to open." As he dealt, he talked about the art and science of poker. His ability to calculate and memorize astounded me, and within twenty minutes he had all my money. It took an hour for him to get all of Eddie's, but only because he had more to lose.

Eighteen hours of hard labor were closing in on me. The one beer I drank made me sleepy, and my eyes were scratchy from lack of sleep and cigarette smoke. I felt myself dozing, and heard Eddie say, *What was the line... "Uh, uh, um"?* and Frank's response, *I think it was "Um, well, uh."*

"Shut up, you guys," I said, forcing myself back awake.

"Okay, game's over," Frank said.

I looked at the money on the table. I suspected Frank had left ten dollars more than my losses. Probably did the same for Eddie, Rolly and Troy. For Frank it was about the game, not the money.

To wake ourselves up, we stood on the Plymouth Town Pier, smoking and swapping gossip with Pat Burgess: who had a big haul and where, whose boat was in for repairs, who was knocked up, who had been knocked down, who had been arrested recently and why.

Frank spotted her first and let out a low whistle.

"Whoa Nellie," whispered Rolly.

I was tired but not too tired to admire a young, attractive woman walking toward us. Unsteady on stiletto heels, she carried a large package in both hands. I wasn't surprised when her heel got stuck in a crack in the weatherworn wood, and she nearly stumbled. Helpless, she held the package, tried without success to liberate her captured foot, then looked at us. We three gentlemen/hound dogs silently appraised her dilemma, exchanged glances, and headed over to help.

"Let me," I said, holding out my hands.

"*Grazie.*" She handed me the package. There was no way not to stare at her shapely legs; perched in heels, each curve was clearly defined.

She wore no stockings, but her skin was tanned and looked smooth and soft. When she put her hand on my shoulder for balance, I thought I was going to explode.

She slipped her tiny foot out of the shoe and hovered, uncertainly. A delicate gold chain glittered around her ankle. Pat took off his work gloves, pulled the shoe free, and handed it to her. Still holding my shoulder, she slipped her foot back in. "Captain Stanley is here?"

Mesmerized, I was about to say there was no one named Captain Stanley, when Frank cleared his throat, stepped on his cigarette butt, and identified himself as Frank Savery, captain of the *Stanley.*

"How may I help you?" he asked with the smile that had slayed dozens of unsuspecting women.

"My grandmother, she die last week. She ask I come see you, say *Grazie*. Thank you. From my family." She held out a slender hand and he took it quickly, gently.

All at once, I realized she must be the granddaughter of the little old lady in black. How I knew this, I have no idea; it was a sudden certainty. Something about the way she held her head high. Her dignity and grace.

"I give you this." She reached for the package I was holding for her. I handed it back, and she unwrapped a large dish of custard. "For you. Pizza gaina. We make at Easter and special occasions. Very rich. Eggs, salami, mortadella and capachulla. To thank for the kindness to my mother."

"Many thanks to you." Frank tipped his head and accepted the dish. "Your grandmother was a wonderful lady, and very courageous. I hope all your memories are good ones."

Eddie, Troy, Rolly, and Pat and I murmured, *Yes, she was wonderful, very special, everyone respected her.* But our words of comfort couldn't compare to Frank's. He took a step forward to join her, raised his right hand chest high and said, "Over 100 years ago, Felicia Dorothea Hemens gave us these words in her poem."

"CALM on the bosom of thy God,
Fair spirit, rest thee now!
E'en while with ours thy footsteps trod,
His seal was on thy brow."

Dust, to its narrow house beneath!
Soul, to its place on high!
They that have seen thy look in death
No more may fear to die."

As he finished, he nodded to the young woman, "In the memory of a strong woman, a woman whose strength was beauty. May there always be such women in our lives," he concluded.

Amen, we said as she crossed herself. The perfect eulogy. Short, direct and delivered with sincerity. How I envied him! Without preparation, he recited the poem with perfection, as if it had been waiting there, in his mind, eager for him to speak the lines. Solemnly, she turned and walked away, her head high.

Fire!

I saw the opening maw of hell,
With endless pains and sorrows there;
Which none but they that feel can tell–
Oh, I was plunging to despair.

Herman Melville, Father Mapple's Hymn, *Moby Dick*

As I stepped onto the dock that chilly, overcast September morning, I found it hard to believe that summer was almost over, and I'd be back at school in a few days.

"Your expression is easy to read, Old Dog," Frank greeted me. "But it's only for a few more years."

"Then you can be just like us grown ups," Eddie laughed. He finished a cigarette and flipped the butt into the water. "And someday there'll be a skinny ass brat wanting to go fishing as bad as you do."

"Yeah, right," I smirked. I wanted to say, *Spending the summer with you guys has been like a dream come true,* but it sounded too sentimental. I wanted to express my thanks to Frank. But of course I wasn't going to say either of those things. And fortunately there was no need to, because they knew.

"Winsor's here," Frank said.

Bright and quick like his father; Winsor had the same inclination to look at situations differently from most people. To me, a distinct advantage; however, his teachers spent a lot of time trying to fit him into their box of black and white. He was only 14, but a hard worker who would lighten the load for all of us. A welcome addition on such a dismal day! "Where is he?"

"In the wheelhouse, figuring our course." Frank gestured. "Okay, we're all set."

Rolly changed the kicker over to the Caterpillar engine and all the deck lights came on in a blaze. We hoisted a single scallop dredge on board and set up the old steaking box. This late in the summer the price of scallops was up, so Frank figured we could make the long trip to Georges and still have a decent profit.

The *Andrew and Agnes* and the *Carib* were docked nearby, also getting ready to head out. Frank backed us away from our inside berth at the State Pier and started slowly down the narrow, shallow channel. Eddie stood in the bow acting as lookout until we reached the black and white turn buoy with its white blinking light, soon to be deactivated for the winter.

Almost every port had its own parochial complaint against the Coast Guard. In Plymouth, the irritation centered on the large black and white turn buoy that indicated a critical 90-degree turn in the channel. During the yachting season, amidst the long daylight hours of summer, a white blinking light marked the turn. Early in the fall, the Coast Guard doused the light until the next spring. During those short winter days when fishermen left and returned in cave-like darkness, there was no guiding light. Elmer Boutin, the harbormaster, and the Plymouth Fishermen's Association made repeated requests to maintain the light on a year-round basis, without results.

I stepped into the wheelhouse to see Winsor. "Need help?" A joke. Like Frank, he did calculations quickly and accurately.

"Yeah, Skip, I think my boot is untied. Can you handle the laces?"

"Ha ha ha. You just wanna see me bend over. Want coffee?"

"Sure, thanks."

I went to the fo'castle. Toasty inside, unlike the damp, raw air outside.

"Last trip," Troy said, handing me two cups.

"I know. Will you miss me?"

He pretended to wipe his eyes. "I don't know how I'll live."

I went back up to the wheelhouse, and Winsor and I drank our coffee, relishing the warmth.

Just before dawn a cool northwest wind started to whip off wave tops and push the spray in graceful mare's tails. The dawn held little light, the clouds hung low; gray and wind-streaked. More like October than late summer. Frank and I stood side by side on deck, smoking.

"Ever read anything by T.H. Huxley?" he asked.

"There are a lot of Huxleys and I get them mixed up, but it doesn't matter because I haven't read any of them."

"Well, T.H., Thomas Henry, came first. He was an associate of Darwin. In fact, we have him to thank for the publication of *Origin of the Species*. Darwin sat on his ass for years until Huxley found out someone else with the same theory was about to publish. That's why they call him 'Darwin's Bulldog.'"

"Oh, okay."

"So T.H. was the grandfather of Julian and Aldous. Aldous wrote *Brave New World*, an ironic look at a utopian future. If you look up *utopia* in the dictionary, you'll see it means *no place*. Try to find some time to read it, and we'll discuss it."

"Okay."

He took a long drag. "But I find T.H. more interesting. When he was 21 he signed on the British frigate, *Rattlesnake*, as an assistant surgeon, but he was a botanist at heart. Spent most of his time studying jellyfish and corals and anything else he could find. One of the memorable articles he wrote concerned education."

"Cripes," I said.

"No, just listen. Huxley said, *The only medicine for suffering, crime, and all the other woes of mankind, is wisdom. Teach a man to read and write, and you have given him the keys of the wisdom box. But it is quite another thing to open the box*." Frank chuckled. "I think he made a serious omission by leaving out math, but you get the idea."

"I get the idea," I confirmed in a glum voice. "It's all about school."

"Actually, no, it's all about thinking." Frank tapped his head. "But thinking by itself means nothing, it has to be applied to action. Like when you think about girls..." now he reached over and tapped my head. "*Capice*?"

"Capice," I laughed.

"You can do anything you want to do, but first you must think about what it is you really want. Remember, everything, every mother-loving thing in this universe started with a thought. That new car design, the principles of *pi*, a fathometer and the *Mona Lisa*. They all started with an idea."

"Believe me," I said, "I got no trouble coming up with ideas!"

The northwesterly wind threw cold spray on our stern and the rear of the wheelhouse as we rounded Race Point. The *Reneva* and the *Shirley and Roland* were fishing north of the Highland. Frank pointed in their direction and said, " I'm glad we took the net off and changed to the scallop dredge, otherwise it would be hard to ignore two good fishermen like that." And he inched the throttle up one more notch.

Passing west of the Franklin Swell many hours later, we saw three large scallopers from New Bedford distributed along the southeastern horizon, boats twenty and thirty feet larger than the *Stanley*.

"There's your friend from the Green Mooring," Frank said. "I talked to him a little while ago and he's one man short. He wants to know why you're not in school and if you're getting a full share?"

We both laughed. Our dredge went over quickly and 45 minutes later came back loaded with scallops, a few flounders and some crushed lobsters. Winsor and I filled the cutting box and buckled ourselves in to start shucking the scallops.

"It was a day like this," he said, "that my dad slipped and the towing wire slashed off the tips of two fingers. Rolly wanted to call the Coast Guard but Dad said not to. He just put what was left of his fingers into a bowl of salt to stop the bleeding."

"Jesus."

We worked as fast as we could, but after five tows, the deck was piled high with scallops, and Frank came out to help. I noticed that Rolly was making extra trips to the engine room.

"Is he okay?" I asked Frank.

"He's spooked. He had a nightmare about a fire. Plus he's concerned about one of the gas fittings on the kicker. It's dripping a little."

The late afternoon sky changed to pale green near the horizon, and the clouds took on an innocent peachy color with gray tops. Pink-purple changed to deep purple in just a few minutes, then to black. I looked at Winsor and we were thinking the same thing. In a week we'd be looking at the inside of a classroom!

Over a hearty beef stew supper prepared by Eddie, Frank explained that our schedule for the next three days would be eight hours on and four hours off. Winsor and I had seconds, then thirds, when Eddie told us to scram or there wouldn't be any left for mug ups to sustain us through the night.

To the casual observer, shucking scallops wasn't much different from steaking whiting. But I discovered that the process used all new muscles, and after a few hours each one screamed in pain.

At 1:00 a.m. of our third day, I stretched and groaned. The wind picked up to 20 knots, and by 3:00 it started to rain again. Not a soft gentle mist, but a drenching downpour that left everyone grouchy and shivering. I started counting down the hours before I could go below for four hours of sleep.

At 3:30 we strayed off the sandy gravel bottom and hit some rocks at the northeast edge of our tow. The dredge came back empty due to jagged breaks in the metal rings. Ferocious obscenities flew, and we hurried to make repairs while Frank battled strong winds to bring us back into position. As we steamed slowly forward, icy windblown spray made us all miserable.

"I've had a bellyfulla this. Let's just head for home," Frank said. "We caught 1,500 pounds of scallops, enough for a decent trip." He put his hand on my shoulder. "Skip, you're due for a break."

I didn't argue! The dry heat in the fo'castle derailed my plan for coffee and a cigarette while relaxing in the orange glow of the stove. I flopped into my bunk and fell asleep immediately.

In the middle of a dream about riding a giant turtle with Darwin, I felt someone grab my leg, and Winsor's voice: "Skip! Wake up! There's a fire!"

I sat up and accepted the life jacket he pushed at me. "What? Where?"

"Hurry! We gotta get the hell outa here!"

We ran up on deck. The lights were off, and the thickest, blackest smoke I had ever seen poured out of the engine room, wheelhouse and lazarette. Frank was shouting into the radio, alerting the Coast Guard. Water poured out of our deck hose, so that meant the main engine was still running. Rolly aimed a fire extinguisher at the flames. Winsor had brought another small extinguisher up from the fo'castle, and Eddie grabbed it working alongside Rolly. I blinked, rubbed my eyes, and when I swallowed, I tasted copper. And fear.

Eddie threw down the empty extinguisher. "Skip, we need to get the lifeboat ready!"

Lifeboat? I fought panic as I followed him. The orange dory, one of Frank's favorite summer perches, sat on top of the wheelhouse. My foot slipped as I climbed to the rain-slicked roof. From far away I heard shouting: *Be careful, Skip!* I swung one-handed with the roll of the boat for an instant until I regained my footing.

Eddie was right next to me. "Throw this crap into the fish pen!" We grabbed spare buoys, twine, floats and an ancient box of jelly donuts, squirreled away over the summer. Climbing in, I found the thole pins tied to the seats, just as they should be. I also found the bottom plug used to keep the boat from filling up with rainwater and stomped it into place with my heel.

Eddie cleared the pulleys to lift the dory over the side. "Capt, we're all ready, you want this in the water?"

The smoke was too thick to see Frank, but we could hear his answer: "No, hang on, hold up. It's damn close, but we may not need to do that. It might come under control as long as the engine continues running. Just stay there for now. The Coast Guard is sending the eighty footer from P'town for us and John Pinto isn't far away."

"Damn," I gasped. Calling the Coast Guard was the ultimate humiliation for someone like Frank. He would have preferred open heart surgery with one of Eddie's knives to the psychological torture of asking for help; the big, powerful Coast Guard cutter dragging us through the waves like a large dog trying to run away from a tin can tied to its tail.

The flames were in retreat, but the smoke increased. The wind swirled it around our faces, covering everyone with oily soot that mixed with rain oozing into our eyes, blinding, stinging.

"Eddie, do you need me up here, or should I go down and start the hand pump? There's a lot of water in the bilge and it'll be on the scallops pretty soon."

"Right, go ahead, we don't want to lose our trip."

I slid down; careful not to lose my foothold, thinking I must be a real fisherman to be worried about our catch instead of the danger.

Frank picked up the two-way to speak to the *Liberty II*.

"We're on our way," Pinto said. "We saw the flames from here. Need us to pick anyone outa the water? Looked as though you were going down for sure."

"No, it was a close thing. Too close, John. If we can get the smoke under control and keep the engine running we should be all set," Frank said. "Everyone was great. If anyone had panicked, it woulda been a different story. I'll let you know when we're under way again. Over and out." He gestured for Rolly, and they made their way down to the engine room, spraying everything in front of them with the fire extinguishers. The rest of us gathered in the wheelhouse; no one felt like going down into the dark fo'castle yet. Either the fire, or the water we used, had partially cut the electrical power. Huddled in the cramped wheelhouse, we heard banging, thumping and clanging, as Frank's commentary kept us abreast of progress: *Sonova bleeding whore! I dropped the mother-fucking flashlight! Damn it! Damn it all to hell and back!* Then Rolly's gentle response, *Take it easy, Capt, I got another one right here.*

More clanking, more swearing, and then, unexpectedly, a beautiful, familiar sight: light! Frank and Rolly emerged from the engine room with grins of triumph. Faces covered in sweat and black soot, they looked like poorly made up minstrels.

"Who's the ass kicker?" Frank demanded, throwing his arm around Rolly. "Seriously! Who tha hell kicks the ass of this mother loving boat?"

We cheered, slapped backs. *Rolly! Rolly!*

Then Frank turned to Winsor. "How far to Provincetown?"

"Thirty minutes, the Race is just off our port bow."

"Okay, head us to Plymouth. We need our insurance guy and somebody to fix the problem so we never have to deal with this again. It's going to take a while and a mountain of money to get this put back together." He looked at me. "Just as well you're headed back to school, Skip. No telling when we'll be back on the water. But we got through, and that's what counts. Great work, everyone. Rolly, let's get some of the foam cleaned up. Skip and Troy, check the scallops."

Enjoying the steady rumble of the engine, we split up to carry out Frank's orders. I saw the rest of the scallops had been shucked while I slept, and were tucked into their icy beds. Back on deck I cleared out more bilge water with the hand pump.

"Christ!" I heard Eddie shout.

I stopped and looked up. "What now?"

Eddie pointed. "Hang on to your skivvies. We're about to be rescued."

"Shit shit shit!" Frank grabbed the radio's speaker. "This is the *Stanley*. Our problem has been repaired, and we will not, repeat, will *NOT* require assistance!"

The Coast Guard issued an angry, ear-splitting response complaining that we had called them out for nothing, wasted their time, etc, etc. Frank flipped them a bird, but his voice remained polite. "Thanks for your help. But we're all set. Over and out."

To my surprise, they continued bearing down on us, circled around our stern, and opened fire at some imaginary objects with their forward deck gun. Official target practice. With their throttles wide open, they would be home long before us.

"Arrogant, supercilious, assholes," Frank said, as he waved cheerfully.

Frank called his wife on the Boston Marine Radio and told her to call mothers, girlfriends, and spouses to let them know we were okay. Several hours later we steamed past the Gurnet, Bug Light and Beach Point. The only people we really wanted to see were the Reliable Fish Buyers so we could unload and go home, but a police cruiser, ambulance, reporter, fire truck and insurance representative were waiting for us.

"The Coast Guard called ahead to say we were on our way," Frank said. "Since we had a fire, the fire department is required to make an inspection. Don't speak to anyone, let me do all the talking. Okay?"

We all nodded, glad to let him handle the questions, which he did with professional patience.

The insurance agent left first, thankful that the insured was still afloat. The fire department poked around the engine room and lazarette. The reporter told the photographer to get plenty of shots of us–sooty, bleeding, smelling like burnt rubber, aching to wash up and change clothes. The story with the picture was front page news in the *Old Colony Memorial*: "Calm Efforts Save Dragger From Complete Destruction, Crew Puts Out Bad Fire Aboard Savery Scallop Boat Off P-Town." Always intensely proud, the page one position in the newspaper hurt Frank more than any physical blow. But as he said, *It could have been a lot worse!*

And that was the thing with Frank. He didn't just dispense wisdom. He lived it. Spread it. Three months ago he'd taken an arrogant, headstrong kid under his wing and taught him the value of leadership; of earning respect, taking risks and appreciating what makes life an adventure. My time on the *Stanley* ushered in a maturity I hadn't expected or possessed before. I would return to school as a serious student and apply what I had learned, and I would get good grades and continue my education, maybe get a college degree. Something that would not have happened if not for his lessons. Eddie had once said of Frank, *What a man he is, what a man he is. There will never be another like him. Never.*

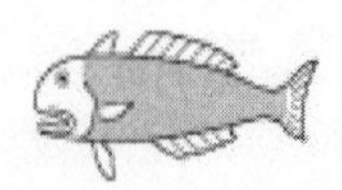

Walking home, I didn't notice any of the familiar surroundings, because in my fantasy it was the beginning of summer and I was back on the *Stanley*. Approaching the Gurnet, we pass close to the number one buoy; my beautiful, welcoming mermaid, dancing in our wake. I lean way over and try to touch her, but she's out of reach. And I hear her gentle whisper: *Come back.*

Afterword

I spent three summers and most of my winter school vacations on the *Stanley*. In the fall of 1953, Frank sold the *Stanley* to Reliable Fish Company. Two days after Thanksgiving she sank on the backside of Cape Cod, west of the Nauset buoy.

In June of that year I graduated from Plymouth High School. Everyone, including me, expected that I would go work on Frank's new boat, the *Libby*, but Frank's advice was too good to ignore: *Go to Alaska!* It seems hard to imagine now, but land was free in the territory of Alaska. Frank said, Just *go and claim yours!* And so I bought a one-way ticket on a Pan Am flight, planning to purchase another ticket after I'd earned the money to return home in the fall. But Alaska proved too alluring. Fishing, flying, gold and a good job all conspired to keep me in Fairbanks until the prospects of being drafted became reality. I gave my house away as a wedding present to Phil Nobel, my roommate and the person who helped me prove my land claim, and returned home. The next week I joined the Marine Corps. There were many times during my stint at boot camp that I longed to be back at sea!

On Wednesday, July 25, 1956, at 11:10 PM, the Stockholm and the Andrea Doria collided off Nantucket. Several hours later, before dawn, another physically violent event took place on the fishing grounds near Nantucket. This trauma occurred inside Frank Savery's head as he suffered a brain seizure. Fortunately, there were at least eight Coast Guard vessels at the Andrea Doria site nearby. One of them arrived shortly after Eddie and Rolly called for help. A rescue cutter came alongside the *Libby* in fifteen-foot seas, and despite the excruciating pain in his head, Frank would not be transferred in a wire basket. "I'm not ready for the casket--basket yet," he said as he made the leap to the cutter.

I was stationed at White Beach, Okinawa, when the letter from my mother arrived with news that Frank Savery had suffered a seizure while at sea. Doctors removed a large brain tumor, but it was too late. He remained alert and quick-witted, spending his last days in bed reading English poets and drinking Scotch whiskey. He died in the summer of 1957. He was 52.

He would have been the first to declare, *Life goes on with or without my big fat say!* and sure enough, it did. In 1960 I was working in the Radiology Department of Faulkner Hospital when I met a student nurse named Carolyn Baker. She agreed to go to a Bruins game with me after my date stood me up (one thing I have learned is that nothing happens by chance!). We were married soon after, and our first child, Susan, was born in 1961 while we were living in Jamaica Plain. Our son, Peter, was born in Hyannis in 1964.

My father gave up drinking almost immediately after the birth of his first grandchild. His addiction had been at its worst during my stint on the *Stanley*, and my mother had forbidden him to drive a car or set foot in his boat, despite his love of the water. Sober, he was intelligent, sensitive, and displayed a courage that filled me with admiration. Our once dysfunctional family came back together again. We tried to put the past behind us, live in the present, look forward to the future, and make up for lost time. My father died in 1976, after complications from cancer surgery on his face and jaw. I'm sure he would take great pleasure in knowing that his grandson and great-grandsons fish regularly with the rods inscribed *To Peter, From Pappy.*

My mother re-married in 1979 to a man she met at the Foster Grandparents Program. Carolyn and I hosted a small wedding; the prelude to a brief but happy marriage that ended three years later when he died. In 1999 she was 91 and showing the first signs of losing her mental and physical capacities. A nursing home was out of the question; no one dared even suggest it. My mother had been born in that house, had lived with two husbands and raised two sons there. On a sweltering July day in 1999, she consulted with my 95-year old Aunt Gladys about which was her most flattering bathing suit and cap, then waded into the ocean. Never one for prolonged farewells, she drowned in four feet of water less than 100 yards away from the room where she was born.

Eddie Fairweather is 87 years young, actively mowing lawns for younger women in his neighborhood, where he is very selective about his clientele. A picture of him with the white shark has been published on the web (http://newenglandsharks.com) by Captain Tom King. Shark experts from Italy, Sweden, California and around the world have speculated on why a usually warm water fish, probably a juvenile male, was out of its normal range. Perhaps like young Eddie, he just yearned for a change of scenery and a new place to fish.

Rolly Bedard retired from the *Christopher Andrew*, a classically beautiful, modern dragger working out of Scituate, Massachusetts. Most mornings you can find him on the Scituate Fish Pier looking out over the harbor, discussing the catch with other fishermen.

Bob Gloyd served in the Air Force, married his high school sweetheart, Marilyn Clark, and is now working in an engineering group at Intel helping to design the microprocessors that power the Internet.

Pat Burgess' father gave up drinking at the same time my father did, and like my father, turned into a loving parent and grandparent. Pat is now a grandfather himself, fifteen times, and enjoys five great grandchildren. He and his wife Gail live in Kingston, Massachusetts.

Usually it was some small incident that yielded Frank's individual lessons. Take every opportunity to learn something new. Always see the extraordinary in the ordinary. Respect the beliefs of others. Think long and hard about all things, the ugly and sublime, the known and the unknown, then transform the thoughts into action. Put them all together, and they make this irrefutable Truth: everyday we are confronted with opportunities to choose who we want to be. Frank believed our actions and reactions are clear demonstrations of whether we are insecure, narrow minded, and unhappy; or at peace with ourselves and our fellow inhabitants on this small, fragile planet. How Frank would love knowing that his grace and wisdom have served me so many times over the years! As I write this, I sense his presence, and wonder, Does he now believe in God? I hear him laugh. *Skip, I believe in it all!*